MW00811332

CHEW TOY OF THE GNAT GODS

CHEW TOY OF THE GNAT GODS

Reflections on the Wildlife of the Southeast Coast

BRUCE LOMBARDO

*Illustrations and Art by
Carol Johnson-Unser*

Cherokee Publishing Company
Atlanta, Georgia
1998

Library of Congress Cataloging-in-Publication Data

Lombardo, Bruce, 1956-
    Chew toy of the gnat gods : reflections on the wildlife of the
southeast coast / Bruce Lombardo ; illustrations and art by Carol
Johnson-Unser.
      p.   cm.
    ISBN 0-87797-273-7 (trade paper : alk. paper)
    1. Coastal animals -- South Atlantic States. I. Title.
QL157.S68L65   1997
591.75'1'0975 -- dc21   97-34195
                                        CIP

This book is printed on acid-free paper which conforms to the American
National Standard Z39.48-1984 *Permanence of Paper for Printed Library
Materials.* Paper that conforms to this standard's requirements for pH, alka-
line reserve and freedom from groundwood is anticipated to last several
hundred years without significant deterioration under normal library use
and storage conditions.

Manufactured in the United States of America
First Edition
ISBN: 0-87797-273-7
02 01 00 99 98   10 9 8 7 6 5 4 3 2 1
Edited by Alexa Selph
Design by Kenneth W. Boyd and Pamela Haury Kohn
Cover art by Carol Johnson-Unser

 Cherokee Publishing Company
P O Box 1730, Marietta, GA 30061

To my mother, Jean Lombardo, who consistently responded to each of my many childhood inklings about what I wanted to be when I grew up, be it a chef, actor or naturalist, by linking me with the appropriate resources and mentors by week's end.

Contents

Preface

It is two o'clock in the morning, and my skin is on fire. I am, quite literally, being eaten alive. I have no mosquito netting over my bunk in the sea turtle project shack, and the screening in the windows is replete with holes. Not that it would make any difference if they were perfectly sound. The bloodthirsty designs of the tiny sand gnats are not the least bit thwarted by ordinary window screening anyway, or even ordinary mosquito netting, for that matter. Their minute bodies crawl easily through all but specifically designed gnat-proof mesh. I pull the sheet over my face for as long as I can stand it, until the stifling heat forces me to face my invisible enemy again. On and off goes the sheet, on and off in a somnolent cycle of alternating misery and suffocation, until finally, from the sea comes the divine wind that blows and scatters the menacing hordes back to the mainland.

It was in such a state of tortured sleep and semiconscious delirium that the title of this book came to me in the still heat of a windless night in mid-June on Pritchard's Island in South Carolina.

These stories and reflections come from a section of our country demarcated by the Georgia Bight—the indentation in the Atlantic coastline that begins scalloping westward at Cape Hatteras, along the Outer banks of North Carolina, to reach its apogee on the coast of Georgia, then swings back eastward into the Florida peninsula. Here is a section of coast far west of the Gulf Stream, where the maritime waters are warm, shallow, and turbid, where the funneled ocean tides rise and fall an average of nine feet every day, and where the country's greatest tidal marshes serve as the vital nursing grounds for the sea life of the North Atlantic. It is this wide, shallow bay, or bight, that causes a singular portion of our Atlantic coast to lie west, surprisingly enough, of any point on the Pacific coast of South America.

This region of lazy sunsets, Spanish moss, and wild beaches would be a heralded paradise for the nature lover and the beach-goer alike, but for the ominous spirit of the almighty sand gnat, whose unseen host can descend on the innocent at any windless moment, except during the very coldest months of the winter. For the vast majority of the year, they rule our outdoor lives and behavior, and we must obey them. Subjects of their domain enjoy no open-air pursuits without their leave. The naturalist who dares explore these lands must pay homage to this potent presence. While fearful folk find refuge in their air-conditioned sanctuaries, the brave and faithful must be willing to sacrifice their life's blood at the altar of the gnat gods.

They don't call it the Georgia Bight for nothin.'

Introduction
Wilderness Southeast

J ohn "Crawfish" Crawford built a tree house in an oak forest on
the edge of the salt marsh just outside of Savannah, Georgia. From
the front porch you could look out over an enormous expanse of
tidal marsh that gradually faded away to the Atlantic, somewhere
between the islands of Ossabaw and Wassau. The surrounding forest
was a thick tangle of sawtooth palmetto, cabbage palms, and holly
bushes, all overseen by enormous live oak trees, whose spreading
limbs were encrusted with lichens and festooned with long beards of
Spanish moss.

As taken as I was during my first visit to this rich southern set-
ting, I was no less impressed by Crawfish himself. He was a giant of
a man that seemed to have sprung whole from the forest earth itself,
with a shaggy black beard and mane that seemed capable of hosting
habitats of their own. Crawfish was a student of wilderness rather
than universities. He was a walking library of experiential nature
knowledge. Yet as awesome as his capacity for information was, it
was his utter fascination with all things wild that engulfed the visitor.
He had the hyperactive enthusiasm of a six-year-old with a bug jar,
which was rather overwhelming, contained as it was in a body of
such bearlike proportions.

When I first visited him there, I was still a park service naturalist
at Assateague Island National Seashore, in Virginia. I was touched
by the uniqueness of his living arrangements and the sultry beauty of

the wild Southeast Coast, but I never dreamed that I would some-day work for the ecotour company Crawfish had cofounded, let alone actually live in that same tree house, a few years later. I had done a short stint as a naturalist in the Everglades, but otherwise my experience with the Southeast had been somewhat limited. After many years of working as a ranger, however, I was weary of government bureaucracy and ready to try my hand at a different kind of naturalist work, with a nonprofit educational organization.

Wilderness Southeast (WSE) offers natural history tours to wilderness areas throughout the southeastern states, from the Smoky Mountains to the Florida Keys. My first year as a wilderness guide there required a lengthy crash course in the natural history of the Southeast. And in this I was aided greatly by the other WSE natural-ists, Crawfish not the least. The organization's other cofounders, Dick and Joyce Murlless, had a solid base in the field of education, and taught me much about the techniques needed in my role as an interpreter of the wild mysteries of the Southeast Coast.

I eventually became program director for WSE, and over the next six years I spent almost as much time guiding, hiking, and pad-dling through the many wilderness areas of the Southeast as I did in my own home, which, during the years I lived in that tree house at least, was not much different from camping in the woods anyway. I quickly learned to feel just as much at home in the great Okefenokee Swamp, the wild barrier islands of Georgia, the Blue Ridge Moun-tains of North Carolina, or the Florida Everglades. These special places, and many more like them, are a part of my soul now. They glow vividly within my memory, and I feel the need to share them with others, even though I've stopped guiding people through them. This book is an expression of that need.

After Crawfish left it to me, the tree house became my biological station. I watched the subtle change of southern seasons and tried to keep my hand on the pulse of the lives of other species with which I shared my home. An armadillo lived under the house. In my "bed-room hallway," as I often referred to the path that led to the tree house, it was not uncommon to encounter sleeping corn snakes and copperheads. My evenings were serenaded by chuck-will's-widows and the mellow hooting of great horned owls. And when the wind blew off the marsh at low tide, the whole surrounding forest was permeated with the humid aroma of fresh oyster bisque.

Always an amateur student of phenology, the study of seasonal changes, I kept a notebook of the observations I made. Eventually I wrote a weekly nature column. During my seventeen years as a naturalist, I have learned that from all the natural world has to offer, people relate most readily to other animals most like themselves. Strict scientists will have to forgive me for personifying these creatures as I do, but it is part of the license we interpreters take.

Through these accounts of the seasonal happenings in the lives of southern wildlife, I hope the reader will catch some glimpses of the warm ocean waters, dune-lined beaches, cypress swamps, piney woods, meandering rivers, tidal salt marshes, and maritime forests that make up the rich, subtropical world of the Southeast Coast.

January

First Week of January
The Uninvited Roommate

"There's been a wild animal in my house," I thought to myself. What other explanation could there be? The first quarter of my telephone book was missing. Not ripped away in one piece either. The torn edges of the remaining stubs did not match up. They had been torn off page by page!

Some folks, perhaps, would have reacted with dread to the conclusion I had reached, but you must understand, naturalists are a peculiar lot. I was actually kind of happy about it. And I was intrigued. Here was a mystery to puzzle out. I suspected that I had a new and unanticipated roommate in the somewhat dilapidated cottage that was then my home. But who?

After leading a long expedition in the tropics, I had returned to this old house in a marsh-edge wood lot, after an absence of about a month. I searched the house for other signs of my uninvited guest, but could find none. I began to suspect some varmint had merely entered my house to steal material for a nest outside.

It was early January and the cottage was cold. "Time to light up the wood-burning stove," I thought. But, search as I might, I couldn't find the first match anywhere, not the usual stack in the bathroom, nor the big box of kitchen matches by the gas cookstove. I put on an extra sweater.

I returned to the telephone call I had been about to make when I had noticed the condition of the Southern Bell white pages. Sitting on the old sofa, waiting for someone to answer, I looked down at my feet on the floor. Between them, barely sticking out from under the skirting of the couch, was a piece of bright yellow plastic. I drew it from under the sofa. It was a favorite relic of my childhood, a windup submarine bath toy. While asking myself, "Now how did this get here from the bathroom?" I noticed another bright something sticking out from under the couch. Still holding the ringing receiver to my ear, I knelt down, lifted the skirting, and peered under the sofa. There was all sorts of stuff under there! I hung up the phone. Somebody's been hiding my things, things from all over the house, under the couch! How weird!

Standing in front of the sofa, I pulled the high back toward me with a heave. Immediately, I heard a sound like grain pouring from a large sack. Small, dark, round objects were spilling out from under the sofa and rolling all over the floor. I dropped the sofa back with a start. I bent to examine them: palm berries—hundreds of them. "What is going on here?"

Just then, I saw much the same question expressed on the upturned face of a small startled creature that had stumbled hesitantly, like a sleeper rudely awakened, from beneath the couch. Our eyes met. For a brief moment, we examined each other, my new roommate and I. Simultaneously, our two sets of eyes widened. "Yikes, a RAT!" "Eeek, a HUMAN!" The creature, now fully awake, darted for the old cat door (obviously of a former tenant) and was gone. It was clear that each of us had falsely believed that we had the cottage to ourselves. We were both surprised to learn of the existence of a roommate. The smaller of us wisely conceded, at least for the present.

Even a naturalist would not be delighted to find a rat living in his own home. I had a suspicion, however, that this was not a rat of the urban variety. As I pulled the couch over and looked underneath, my suspicions were more than confirmed. This was no ordinary rat. What I found was the most amazing animal nest I had ever seen or hope to see.

Despite the havoc I had wreaked on it by turning it over, it was clearly evident that this nest—dare I say "nest," no, this home, was a work of pride and artistic sensibility, all within the open box of wire springs that supported the sofa cushions. It was neat, orderly, and well organized. What's more, it was tastefully decorated with very colorful and interesting objects, all of them borrowed from me.

At one corner of the wire spring framework, was the master bedroom, a basketball-sized sphere of finely chewed dried grass, with a fist-sized inner chamber, lined with soft natural fibers. At the opposite corner was the pantry, a paper platform, from which the many palm berries had poured, presumably stored for the long winter. Occupying the rest of the space between these two essential rooms were the phone book pages, each carefully torn in thirds, and arranged within the sofa spring framework in such a way as to resemble white walls in the winding hallway of a private art gallery. On display, at intelligent intervals throughout, were the carefully chosen objets d'art. Upon examination, each of these cherished items clearly fell into one of two distinct categories. The first category we'll call "the visually appealing." To my roommate, this concept apparently translated as bright colors and shininess. Included, among other baubles, were all nine of my hard-won Mardi Gras doubloons (he must have carried them, one by one, from the stash in my bedroom) and the aforementioned submarine (a real eye-catcher, believe me).

The second category was more difficult to figure. It included, among other things, every box of matches in the house and a half-full bottle of Windex from the kitchen! That these adornments were greatly treasured by their new owner was evidenced by the gargantuan task of dragging a heavy glass bottle of noxious cleaning solution, from the opposite end of the house. That such objects were carefully chosen was also clear. He took the pepper shaker, but not the adjacent salt shaker of identical size and shape. He walked the narrow kitchen shelf of cooking spices and chose from the very middle, the small, square can of bay leaves. The rest of the many spices, stacked closely side by side, were rejected.

What clued me to the common element of the second category was the bottle of insect repellent he had procured. These other items: spices, sulfurous matches, ammonia compounds—I believe were chosen for their odors. Either he was concerned that his abode possess a clean fragrance with a touch of spicy incense, or he did, indeed, intend to repel pests from his nest. Either of these theories would be in keeping with the cleanliness of his home. Nowhere was there the barest trace of rat droppings, dirt, or discarded palm berry hull. No ordinary rat, this one.

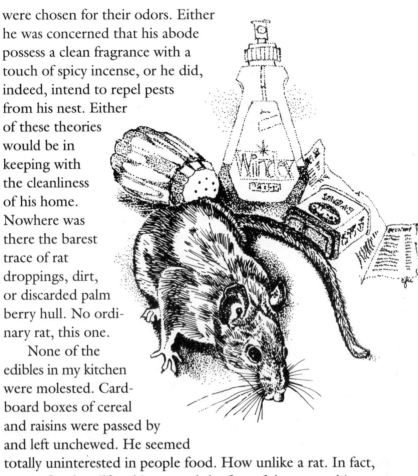

None of the edibles in my kitchen were molested. Cardboard boxes of cereal and raisins were passed by and left unchewed. He seemed totally uninterested in people food. How unlike a rat. In fact, except for the pilfered items and the fate of the poor white pages, I would never have known he was in the house if I hadn't looked under the couch.

By now, perhaps you may have guessed the identity of this mystery creature. He was an eastern wood rat, also known as a "packrat." The word "packrat" has permeated our descriptive language ever since pioneers discovered the peculiar behavior of this native American rodent. No immigrant wharf rat from the crowded ports of Europe, the wood rat avoids cities and is shy of people, rarely moving into any but the most abandoned of rural human habitations. They prefer lowland forests with spreading live oaks and lots of palmettos. Like a modern-day health-conscious yuppie, packrats shun junk food. Their diet consists of only natural greens, nuts, and berries.

Although they are about the same size, wood rats look notably different from the Norway and black rats that followed our forebears here from the old world. Wood rats have tails covered with fine hair, instead of the naked, scaly tails of the "introduced" species. Also, wood rats have white feet and bellies, fawn-colored pelts, larger ears, and larger eyes (for their nocturnal foraging in dense forests), all of which work to give them a more endearing appearance.

But their renowned eccentricity is their most endearing quality. There is a legend that the packrat, occasionally overcome by guilt over his chronic kleptomania, will leave token gifts in return for the pilfered item. You go to recover the bright red shotgun shell that you left on the workbench in the barn last night, and you find in its place a hickory nut! This very real tendency, especially pronounced in some western wood rat species, is perhaps misunderstood. It is not conscience that motivates this trade, but avarice. So overcome by the beauty of the shiny pop top in his path, the packrat will drop any mere food item he may have been carrying in his mouth, and steal away, totally absorbed with his newest treasure.

Second Week of January
The Gentle Giant

"They won't eat me. They won't eat me. They're vegetarians. They don't eat people." These are the words you find yourself whispering over and over into your snorkel tube when you encounter your first manatee. Manatees are huge, and they seem even more so when you are floating in the same murky water they are. They can be more than ten feet long and weigh over a ton. Yet no one has ever been injured by a manatee. They are completely harmless—no horns, no fangs, no claws. It's the size of these gentle giants that is so intimidating, and that's no accident. There are few predators big enough to take on an adult manatee. Even so, our species, the West Indian manatee, is critically endangered.

Few of us see the manatees as they graze along the Southeast Coast in the summer, because they are very quiet and shy. Unless you happen to be looking at just the right spot on the water's surface, at just the right moment, you'll never know they're down there. They never come up out of the water. But, like other marine mammals (dolphins, seals, etc.), manatees must breathe air. For this purpose, they stick their nostrils., and sometimes their entire heads, out of the water. Occasionally, if you are sitting quietly on a dock, or fishing from a boat, you'll hear them rather than see them. They exhale explosively and inhale quickly, not unlike a dolphin. Manatees, however, can hold their breath a lot longer than dolphins, because they are much less active. It doesn't take enormous energy to subdue seaweed.

Manatees are unique among marine mammals because they are herbivores. They will eat almost any aquatic or marine vegetation. Our sleek dolphins and the frisky seals of the north are fish hunters, streamlined and muscular, built for speed. By comparison, a manatee is a sluggish forager with a blobby body resembling an unfinished Play-doh project. Their diet and sedate lifestyle have earned them the appropriate nickname "sea cow." In addition to the various sea-weeds along our coast, Manatees will graze the salt marsh cordgrass at high tide. The summer pastures of the sea cow are the vast tidal marshes of the Southeast Coast, as far north as Virginia. But by this time of year, the manatees have long since returned to the Florida Peninsula for the winter.

It is in Florida that manatees run into their biggest trouble. With an average of over one thousand people moving to Florida every day, the state's coastline is changing rapidly and drastically. Everyone, it seems, wants to retire to Florida, and they all want waterfront property. Manatee habitat is disappearing.

Despite their ample layer of blubber, the manatees' vegetarian diet does not provide them with enough energy to withstand cold winter waters. Manatees are vulnerable to hypothermia. During colder weather, they will congregate in large numbers around some of Florida's deep spring heads, which have constant water temperatures year-round. Unfortunately, some manatee wintering grounds are in areas heavily used for recreational boating. Considering the endangered status of this species, a horrifying number of collisions occur in some areas. So many adult manatees have prop scars on their backs and tails that manatee researchers regularly use the scars to identify individual manatees. Many of the collisions result in manatee fatalities. In addition, waterfront development leaks herbicides and other pollutants into manatee grazing areas, and the toxins accumulate in their bodies.

It is at a few of these wintering grounds that snorkelers may have the rare opportunity to come face-to-face with a manatee. Here, it is vital that snorkelers and divers understand the proper code of conduct: Never disturb or touch a manatee, or approach too closely. Manatees that are too often chased from the warmer spring water, or away from important grazing sites, can become weakened and sick in winter.

The experience of watching a manatee through your snorkel mask is thrilling. On warmer days, the manatees stray further from the spring head, where the water is murkier. You may see the silhouettes of these huge creatures rising from the depths beneath you to take a breath. Your heart races. You recite your mantra about the manatee's diet, as the ominous theme from Jaws rises unbidden from the dark recesses of your mind.

In the clearer water nearer to the spring head, you can see them for what they really are, innocent animals without a hint of malice. They are so unattractive they are endearing. Here, near the spring, you may observe how they graze and interact, or watch mothers suckling their young. You can see the thick, gray hide and the toe-nails on their front flippers—both reminiscent of elephants, their distant kin. A few manatees in these areas have learned to trust people and actually approach snorkelers, begging for strokes and scratches. The young seem especially curious about us. If you are lucky, you may even get kissed.

When you get to know these gentle giants with whom we share the planet, they make a lasting imprint on your heart. What a pity; what a sadder world would be left to us, if here, in the most affluent nation on earth, we choose faster boats, greener lawns, and higher real estate profits over the continued existence of one of the earth's most precious creatures, the manatee.

Third Week of January
The Flight of the Squirrel

The very idea of a squirrel that can fly sparks the imagination. (Indeed, the idea inspired a cartoon show.) It is not uncommon to see our native gray squirrels make dazzling leaps from branch to branch. But what would it be like to watch a squirrel spread its "wings" and glide from tree to tree. Most folks would express surprise if told that flying squirrels are common residents of the Southeast. In some places they are actually more abundant than gray squirrels.

So why don't we ever see them? The answer is simple. Unlike most kinds of squirrels, flying squirrels are nocturnal. In fact, they are among the most strictly nocturnal of our native wildlife. They are never active during the day or even at dusk. These tiny squirrels, with large, dark eyes for seeing at night, venture out of their dens only well after the sun has set. They glide between trees with complete silence, never touching the ground, collecting fruits and nuts while still fresh on the trees.

Flying squirrels do not really fly. Rather they glide. Also, a flying squirrel does not actually have wings, but flaps of skin that stretch from their wrists to their ankles. These gliding flaps fold neatly at their sides when not in use, which is usually the case. They spend a lot more time scurrying amongst tree limbs than they do gliding to the next tree. But when they do glide, it is a sight to behold. Since they cannot fly upward, they will usually leap from the upper limbs

of one
tree to
the trunk
of the
next. They
stretch out
their flaps
and glide speed-
ily to their destina-
tion, sometimes over
forty feet away, landing
with a soft, but distinc-
tive click when their
claws grab the tree bark.
The unique tail of the flying
squirrel is wide and very flat, serving
as a rudder with which to steer through
the darkness.

They are much more social than other
squirrel species, especially during this time of
year. In general, their interactions seem more playful
than territorial. Except during the breeding season, when mated
pairs have their own nests, flying squirrels tend to live in groups,
sometimes of over twenty individuals. Within these clans, the members generally have winter stores in common and get along amicably,
unlike the continually feuding gray squirrels. Also unlike their gray
cousins, who hide individual nuts throughout their territory, flying
squirrels tend to collect large caches of food near their nest to sustain themselves through the winter.

Like most squirrels, their favorite nest sites are in hollow trees or
old woodpecker holes. It is for the sake of such cavity nesters as
squirrels, owls, woodpeckers, and raccoons, that dead or dying trees
should be left standing in our parks whenever possible. Occasionally,
however, flying squirrel clans can be a problem, because they are not
above nesting in the attics of old houses in the vicinity of big trees,
the likes of which abound in southern historic districts. Like other

rodents, they tend to convert chewable items (bedding, drapes, etc.) into a form more to their liking for nesting material. Especially this time of year, when they spend more time around their nest site, owners of older houses can sometimes hear them scurrying over ceiling tiles or even through walls.

Look for flying squirrels after dark, around old trees in city parks and older neighborhoods, where nearby street lamps may afford you a glimpse of these unique creatures. Also listen for the very high-pitched squeak, which the squirrels use to communicate with other members of their clan.

Fourth Week of January
The Right Whale
for the Southeast Coast

T he dark bulk came into view out of the fog, along the
endless line of wild beach ahead. It was a chill winter morning on
the Georgia coast. Cathy Sakas, then resident naturalist on Little St.
Simons Island, had been asleep in her warm bed mere moments earlier, when she received an unexpected call from the Department of
Natural Resources. A Coast Guard helicopter had spotted a small
beached whale along Little St. Simons. The report stated that it was
probably a pilot whale, a common small whale species. Would she
please check it out before the high tide returned? As she drove her
Jeep over the sand, through the morning mist, little did she know
that she was about to make a scientific discovery that would solve a
mystery that had long represented a gap in the known life history of
a rare and endangered whale species.

The small whale was lying on its side. It looked dead. As she
approached the whale, she noted immediately that it was the correct
size and color for a pilot whale, black, about fifteen feet long, but
something didn't look right about it. A naturalist for many years,
Cathy had seen plenty of pilot whales swimming off the Georgia
coast. Their most noticeable characteristic when they came up for a
breath was a prominent dorsal fin like a dolphin's. This dead whale
had no dorsal fin at all. It could have been a pygmy sperm whale,

another small species, but when she looked in the mouth, Cathy found no teeth! Pilots and sperm whales, along with other members of the toothed whale family, like orcas, porpoises, and dolphins, have large, sharp teeth, which they use for catching fish and other large prey. But the mouth of this unfortunate whale was filled with rows of sturdy featherlike projections. It was a baleen whale. Such a whale uses its baleen, a special mouth structure, as a fibrous comb with which to filter out shrimplike krill and other small schooling creatures, as it cruises through the ocean, mouth agape. But baleen whales are all huge! Cathy knew of no small baleen whale species. Then she saw it, a fleshy strip of collapsed tubing hanging from the middle of the whale's underside. This anatomical structure could well be the remains of an umbilical cord. If this fifteen-foot individual was a stillborn infant, than its parents had to be whoppers!

She raced excitedly back to her office, reviewing the baby whale's characteristics in her mind: the double blowhole, the strange-shaped mouth, arching downward like a permanent frown. Her book on marine mammals indicated that the beached whale must be an infant of a critically endangered whale species known as the right whale. But right whales were listed as whales of the North Atlantic. What was a baby right whale doing on the Georgia coast? Though understandably doubtful at first, the experts wasted no time in confirming Cathy's extraordinary conclusion.

On the verge of extinction ever since the whaling days of the Moby Dick era, right whales were so named because they were the best source of valuable whale oil, literally the "right" whale. Right whales were so sought after, that their once healthy populations were decimated by the mid-1700s. Though they were actually thought to be extinct at one point, a small population managed to carry on, so that now, about three hundred remain in all the North

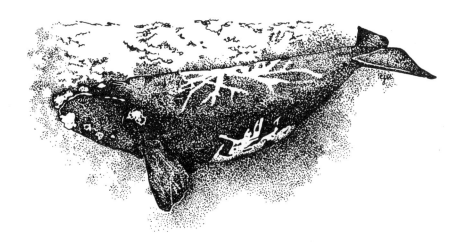

Atlantic. These right whales have long been known to summer off the coast of New England. But they disappear every winter. Come the next spring, the females return to such places as the Bay of Fundy with young calves at their sides. But no one ever knew where the winter calving grounds were, not, at least, until that winter.

We now know that it is the shallow ocean waters of the Georgia Bight, that indentation in the Atlantic Coast between Cape Hatteras and North Florida, that right whale cows seek out for their calving ground. Between mid-November and mid-March, the seventy-foot-long cows frolic and give birth in the balmy Georgia waters. Although they generally remain between five and fifteen miles from shore, they occasionally come in closer. A sea kayaker encountered one just off St. Simons Island a couple of years ago—surely an unforgettable experience. Where the males winter is still uncertain.

It may seem odd that in the late twentieth century, science is still ignorant of such basic life history facts about creatures as big as whales, the largest animals ever to roam the earth. It is very difficult to study such wide ranging marine mammals. If you ever find a beached whale, or if you are a boater and you see whales in the ocean, always report your sightings to your state Department of Natural Resources. Note whatever characteristics you can. Does it have a dorsal fin? What color is it? A right whale, because of its split blow hole, has a distinctive V-shaped spout when exhaling. It will also have peculiar white calluslike growths on the top front of its otherwise black head. In fact, each individual has a unique pattern of callosities, enabling airborne researchers to chart the longevity and calving success of individual cows, year after year.

We don't often think of the Southeast as a place for whales. And yet we can be proud that an endangered whale species is now protected by state and federal laws along our coast each winter. And not just any whale, but the rare right whale, the right whale for the Southeast Coast.

February

First Week of February
The Song of the Toad

To the keen-eyed nature observer, the signs of spring are already evident in early February. As the days are lengthening, plants are stirring back to life, and the resident wildlife is turning its attention to reproductive pursuits. One of the very earliest harbingers of seasonal change is the singing of toads.

The song of the southern toad can be heard emanating from the darkness on warmer nights this time of year. Often missed, the toad's song is usually discounted by our brain's subconscious sound filter as just another insect sound. The toad's long, high-pitched trill could easily be mistaken for a cricket call. If traced to its origin, the song will most likely lead you to a roadside ditch filled with water from recent rains.

Like many animals that spend the winter in a kind of slumber, using up stored energy in fat tissues, the toad awakens to the spring not so much hungry as horny. First thoughts are on breeding. To this end, male toads find ephemeral ponds where they join in primeval chorus to beckon females to their nuptial embrace. This embrace can last for days among toads. The male wants to be sure to be in position when the female releases her eggs. Toad eggs are produced in long, coiling, gelatinous strings. Take a lamp pull-chain. Attach it to many other such chains, end to end. Paint them black. Coat them with a generous layer of any clear, whitish slime; egg white will do. Voilà, you have a reasonable facsimile.

That the pond is ephemeral is important. For one thing, on many of the marsh islands along the Southeast Coast, these rain pools are often the only fresh water available. But even near a permanent body of fresh water, toads will favor temporary ponds because in these there are no fish or other predators. Fish are fond of toad eggs.

How do you tell the difference between a male and female toad? Well, it isn't easy. And apparently, in the dark, underwater, so driven by the sex hormones coursing through their tiny brains, it can even be difficult for toads to tell the difference. Upon finding what he thinks is a female, a male will mount her back and wrap his arms around her body, under her arms. But cases of mistaken identity are not uncommon. For this reason, male toads have a special call.

By inducing males to make this special call, it is possible for us to determine toad gender this time of year. The technique is sometimes

referred to as "toad tickling." Pick any toad and, using your thumb and forefinger, gently grasp the toad under its arms from behind. If it remains silent, it is probably a female. If the toad produces a grunting croak, it is a male. This croak, that special call, avoids what, in toad etiquette, would surely be considered a gross faux pas committed by overeager males. This call might well be translated as "Hey, watch it, buddy."

Late winter is the only time southern toads spend their days in water. Soon after the eggs are laid and spontaneously fertilized, the parents return to their terrestrial existence. Toads often live in quite arid habitats, even beach dunes. Toads, unlike frogs, have rough, warty skin that prevents the loss of their precious body fluid to the dry environment around them. Each bump on their skin is capable of producing a toxin that makes them quite unpalatable by most predators' standards. A few garter snakes, for example, are resistant to this toad skin poison and will readily make a meal of a toad.

The wartiness of their skin once gave rise to the idea that handling toads was the cause of warts on humans. Though this myth was debunked long ago, the true cause of warts wasn't discovered until fairly recently. Still a bit of a mystery, it is now known that warts are caused by viruses.

Like frogs, toads go through a tadpole stage after hatching in these ephemeral ponds. Toad tadpoles develop more quickly than most true frog species. For a short time, toad tadpoles eat algae and other vegetation until they sprout legs and absorb their own tails, becoming very tiny toads. By late spring, these quarter-inch-long animals are found in great numbers invading road, field, and forest floor, gobbling up any small insects they can find with a flick of their tiny tongues. Few survive to adulthood. But those that do, do their part in reducing the insect hordes of summer.

Second Week of February
Safety in Numbers

*T*he air is filled with sound—a cacophony of many rusty wagon wheels all turning at once. Uncountable blackbirds are gathered in the spreading oak tree overhead. There is constant movement. Starlings are darting about. Grackles are jostling for better perches in the topmost twigs. Then suddenly, a sound like the crashing of the surf against a sea wall, and the enormous flock is aloft. Almost as if each bird is but a unit in a superorganism, the flock takes off all at once. Now there is complete silence as the blackbirds wheel through the air over the live oak. The contrast of the silence after the raucousness of moments before is almost startling. Then the birds begin to land, hesitantly, perching in the same oak. The squeaking and squawking commence all over again, but only for a minute or two before the flock erupts once more and the cycle is repeated. They don't seem to be able to sit still. They are so skittish. What do these birds have to be so nervous about?

Surely the life of a bird is free and easy—flitting about, eating bugs and berries at your leisure. Of course you must keep an eye out for the local house cat, but merely take flight, and she is a harmless furry thing down on the ground. "Oh," says the robin, "if only it were so simple." A bird's wings do indeed remove him from many threats. But, especially this time of year, there are certain threats where flight is no advantage—aerial predators who fly fast, with needle-sharp claws and a voracious appetite.

The bird flock is like a herd of gazelles on a three-dimensional plane. Regularly the herd is scanned by the hungry eyes of the cheetah, looking for the slow one, the preoccupied one, the weak one. In a herd, you don't want to stand out. Blend in. Move when the rest of them move, and move fast. It is the same with flocks of birds. Don't fly fast enough and you'll be grabbed by strong talons, plucked by a fearsome beak, and served for dinner. So acute is the selective pressure to conform to the movements of the flock that some species have evolved flocking motions so uniform, so choreographed, as to defy the imagination. A sergeant and his drill team would be hard-pressed to execute maneuvers so tight on a two-dimensional parade ground. But these birds do it in midair. As if someone had shouted "about-face!" every member of the flock turns at once. It happens so quickly, time and again. There are no apparent cues, no commands. It seems like magic. Animal behaviorists call this "allelomimetic movement." It is seen in other animals as well, especially in schools of fish, and is born of long ages of being hunted. If you can't hide, then flock together. Many eyes are better than few. Someone is bound to see the predator's approach. Then move as a unit. Don't give the attacker the advantage of choosing from many targets.

In summer, by necessity, many bird species pair off to breed. But when it comes time to migrate, it is better to flock up and remain flocked on the wintering ground, as well. Most birds are gregarious in winter, even if they have to hang out with members of different species. Many winter flocks are mixed-species flocks. Even woodland birds stick close together this time of year. A winter birdwatcher may walk through the forest for an hour and not see a bird. Then suddenly before him is a tree with eleven tiny birds in it, our resident chickadees, titmice, and gnatcatchers, mixed with yellow-rumped warblers down from the north country. But such northern birds did not arrive alone nor travel unmolested. Often on the edge of the migration flock's vision flies a swift, ominous shadow, following the migrants on the long flight south and picking off the stragglers.

Who are these aerial predators that make other birds so wary? They are hawks, of course, but not just any hawk. When we think of hawks, we usually think of the ubiquitous red-tail hawk, the large hawk who soars over fields and along highways, gliding slowly on broad wings, scanning the grasses for field mice and rabbits. But red-tails, and the other large hawk species like them, rarely eat birds. They are slow, powerful hawks designed for soaring and pouncing on terrestrial prey.

Hawks that prey on songbirds must be swift and small enough to be able to maneuver with great agility. Two families of hawks specialize in hunting other birds: the accipiters and the falcons. We rarely notice these less common hawks. They do not soar for long hours overhead. Falcons are like a blur, streaking through the frenzied flock over open ground. The stealthy accipiters stalk the woodlands, perching quietly, then racing in for the attack.

Falcons, like the merlin or the peregrine, are among the fastest animals on earth. The peregrine can dive at speeds approaching two hundred miles per hour. Falcons strike birds in midair. The victim, debilitated by the force of the blow, tumbles to the ground, where he is captured and carried off or eaten on the spot by the falcon.

The accipiters, like the sharp-shinned hawk or the Cooper's hawk, tend to pin their unsuspecting victims to the ground or a tree limb, relying less on speed and more on the element of surprise. While walking through the woods, you may find a pile of feathers on the forest floor, beneath a conspicuous tree limb. This limb was the feeding perch of an accipiter, the spot where he plucked his victim clean and feasted on the still-warm flesh.

Watch any winter flock of birds on the ground in an open area, like the beach or a farm field. When you see them suddenly take flight, stop looking at them. Look up. Look around. Search for a larger bird, moving swiftly overhead or through the ranks on a collision course. This is the best way to actually spot the rare falcons that migrate through, and winter in, the South.

At bird feeders in the suburbs, watch how skittish the birds act. It is unusual to see a lone bird feeding. Once one is brave enough to expose himself at the feeder, others are soon heartened enough to join him. When the birds all dart for cover at once, look for the accipiter, racing toward the feeder or lurking at the edge of the woods.

The prey, however, is not without evasive maneuvers. Allelo-mimetic movement and quick plunges into thick vegetation are the typical responses. But I have seen other birds be more resourceful still. At Sapelo Island, on the Georgia coast, I once watched a pere-grine falcon dive repeatedly on a kingfisher that she had found over a tidepool on the open beach. The kingfisher knew he was too far from the forest to run for cover—he'd never make it. So instead, he found the kind of cover that few other birds could utilize. Each time the peregrine swooped upon him, the kingfisher would dive into the water. It was an amazing sight. The peregrine swooped down on him over half a dozen times, and each time the kingfisher eluded

her. She finally gave up, flying off to seek a less ingenious victim.

Another time, I witnessed an event that could have been a scene from an adventure movie written by songbirds. In this scene, the role of the clever young hero was played by a house sparrow at my feeder. While seated at my desk one winter morning, I heard, "Bump, THUMP," two distinct sounds in quick succession, from the window near the feeder. The second sound was so loud, I wondered if the window might have been cracked. I arose to see what was the matter, and there, on the ground outside, below the window, were two birds, one small, one much larger, lying still. I went outside. As I approached them, the small sparrow rose, still stunned and wobbly, to his feet. After a moment, he regained his whereabouts and flew off. The larger bird, however, never moved again. It was a Cooper's hawk. Its chest cavity was burst open, its breast feathers bloodied, from the impact with the window. Hollywood special effects could not have done a better job on the body of the dead villain in this scene.

I can just imagine the screenplay. Unable to outdistance the antagonist bent on his destruction, our young hero had cleverly lured him into a collision with "the window of death." The resourceful sparrow, in his home territory, knew of the illusion of the window. He gambled that his larger enemy, coming in so fast, would not withstand the greater force of his own impact. The sparrow flew away victorious and freed his true love from the now unguarded dungeon of the evil accipiter. And they both lived ... , or did they fly off into the sunset? Well, you know the rest.

Third Week of February
Laughing Gull

We tend to lump them all together under the term "sea gulls," but there are actually many different kinds of gulls. No one of them is actually named the "sea gull."

If you visit any beach on the Southeast Coast this time of year you will see, huddled together with pelicans and small sandpipers, a number of different gull-like birds. Of these, many will be terns, a distant relative, with shorter legs and straight, pointy beaks. The rest will be gulls of various species and ages, all looking rather similar, with whitish heads held high, blunt beaks, gray wings, white bellies, and webbed feet. Some will have the same shape, but be darker all over and plainer or mottled. These will be the young gulls. In most species, it takes about three years for a young gull to develop typical adult plumage. And in the winter, the plumage of the adults is also faded and somewhat subdued.

Even for the student of nature, it becomes difficult to tell the different gull species apart. But, as the weather warms and breeding season approaches, one of our gull species will become very distinctive. The whitish head will soon turn jet black, from the neck on up, like a black hood. This black-headed gull is named the laughing gull.

Many birds have a muted plumage in winter. Even cardinals become a duller red in winter. A winter plumage can help a bird remain camouflaged during a hard season when he has no reason to call attention to himself. But come spring, it is time to attract a mate

and stake a claim
on a territory,
defending it
against intruding
neighbors. For
this purpose it helps
to possess striking
coloration. Therefore
many birds change
their feathers, or
"molt," as it is
called, in late winter.

The laughing gull is such
a bird. If you watch these gulls
over the next month, you will
see the white and pale gray head
feathers being slowly replaced by dark
black ones, giving a few individuals a salt-and-pepper patchiness. In
summer, you may note that laughing gulls represent the most common gull on the beach. So different is their appearance now, however, that one might easily believe that all those dark-headed gulls of
summer must have migrated south for the winter. But no, at least
some laughing gulls hang out at the beach all year long.

A careful eye can pick them out even now. Look for the smallest
of the gulls. He should have a back and wings that are completely
dark gray, with no contrasting black or white on the wing tips. This
will be the laughing gull in his off-season disguise.

Like other gulls, laughing gulls act as scavengers. They will eat
just about anything, dead or alive, that they can find or steal. It is
not unusual to see them chasing terns or harassing
pelicans. Terns and pelicans are excellent fishermen, catching fish with spectacular headfirst
dives into the ocean. Gulls are inept at fishing, so they often steal fish by bothering
terns and pelicans until they give up their catch. For
the victims of this harassment, it is easier to just go

and catch another fish, than to put up with being pecked and swooped upon. Also, gulls are not above begging, as anyone who has ever had a picnic on the beach can attest. Though such behavior may seem detestable, as scavengers, gulls perform a vital function as nature's beach cleanup crew.

Many gull species have noisy calls that are reminiscent of screaming or cackling. But the call of the laughing gull is almost uncanny: a hearty bird guffaw. If a sea bird were really to laugh, this is what it would sound like. Next time you are enjoying a day at the beach, listen for the sound of gulls laughing. You will undoubtedly hear the distinctive call of our aptly named subject, the laughing gull.

Fourth Week of February
The Big Sleep

She has been sleeping since Christmas. She hasn't eaten a thing so far this year. But, back in January, she gave birth to two cubs. Despite her slumber, she has been nursing them all this time. Some time within the next month, she will emerge from her den, and the baby bears will see the wide world for the first time.

Only a few animal species truly hibernate. Hibernation is a complex metabolic process wherein body functions slow down to near-death levels. Black bears, though they sleep very deeply through the winter, do not actually hibernate. You could pick up a hibernating groundhog and shake him vigorously to no avail. He will not awake until the day appointed by his own internal clock. Shaking a sleeping bear, however, is not advised.

Though they are not found in most of their former range and their numbers have been greatly reduced since the cutting of the great eastern forests, there are still black bears roaming in a few of the Southeast's wilder areas. There are remnant pockets of bear populations found in the southern Appalachian mountains, parts of the Everglades, Ocala National Forest, some of the wilder river basins, and around the Okefenokee Swamp. They need large tracts of forests in which to hunt, and they shun developed areas.

Though their diet is mostly vegetarian, encounters with black bears can be dangerous to unsuspecting hikers if the bear is a sow with cubs. The mother may attack aggressively to defend her brood.

Since she can run up to thirty miles per hour and climb trees as fast as a squirrel, there is no alternative in this frightening situation but to curl up, play dead, and try to appear harmless. This technique usually works, but it is obviously easier said than done. Fortunately such encounters are rare because black bears, after thousands of years of being hunted, avoid humans. They will usually hear or smell you coming and head off in another direction long before you even know you've been near one.

Here in the Southeast, even with our fairly mild winter temperatures, most bears sleep through the winter. It's not that they can't stand the cold. Their thick coats keep them warm enough. And

although food is certainly scarcer in winter, they could still find edible roots and small animals to eat. The reason bears sleep through the winter seems to have more to do with their reproductive behavior than anything else.

One clue to this conclusion is that bears can be seen roaming during winter, but these bears are apparently all males. Male black bears will awaken throughout the winter to forage. But females of reproductive age will spend the autumn gorging on berries, nuts, tubers, honey, grubs, fish, rodents, snakes, and the like, in order to store up fat for the big sleep. Thereafter, she may not even be consciously aware of giving birth to her one to three cubs. Being born during the coldest part of the winter, the nearly naked cubs would be adversely affected were she to leave them to go hunting.

Because the mother bears, though sleeping soundly, can sometimes be awakened if disturbed during the winter, researchers have rather a ticklish assignment when studying bear reproduction in the field. Much about the early days of a cub's life in the wild was discovered only rather recently by such brave men and women. There is a story about two researchers investigating a sleeping bear. Just before sticking their heads into the den, the younger of the two, new to this precarious mode of data collecting, whispers a question, "By the way, what do we do if she wakes up?" The senior researcher calmly replies, "We run like hell." "Wait a minute," says the novice, "I may not have much experience at this, but I do at least know that a person cannot outrun a bear." His partner looks him straight in the eye and answers, "Well, ... I won't be tryin' to outrun the BEAR."

March

First Week of March
Ya Yella-Bellied ... Sapsucker?

Among the many northern birds that migrate to our sunny latitudes to spend the winter is one that leaves his distinctive mark on many of the trees of the Southeast. Keen nature observers often notice neat, orderly rows upon rows of quarter-inch holes willfully drilled into the trunks of magnolias, hickories, and other local trees. These odd patterns are the handiwork of a wild animal called the yellow-bellied sapsucker.

The name is so fanciful that it is familiar to many. Could there really be a bird with such a name here in the Southeast? Yes, in fact, it is a common winter resident, a species of woodpecker. Its appearance is not nearly so flamboyant as its name. The yellow for which it is named is actually quite pale. It looks much like a typical woodpecker. But its behavior is far from that of a typical woodpecker.

Generally, the average woodpecker type does not actually eat trees, of course. They are merely chipping the wood away to expose their prey: the bark beetles and boring grubs that are themselves eating the rotting wood of old limbs and dead trees. Yet no such tree-infesting insects make up a large part of the yellow-bellied sapsucker diet.

Sapsuckers are the exception. They are a type of woodpecker that actually "eats" trees. Or more accurately, they eat the sap of trees. Not unlike the people who produce maple syrup, sapsuckers "tap" trees that have sugary sap. The sapsucker then returns periodically to lick up the sap that leaks from the many holes he has drilled. And if ants or other sugar-loving insects are attracted to the holes, then they just sweeten the pot. The sapsucker is happy to gobble up any insects that come to the bait, as well as the bait itself.

Occasionally, however, the orderly rows of holes drilled by sapsuckers are not so orderly. It seems that as the late winter sun begins to heat up, the sap collecting at the holes ferments and evaporates to higher concentrations. After a morning of slurping fermented sap from dozens of trees, the sapsucker's concentration and sense of order may waver a bit. The results of his labor on such days may be clearly visible for many years afterwards: haphazard rows of holes that are anything but straight.

Although sapsucker holes in tree bark are a permanent fixture of the Southeast, the birds themselves will be leaving us soon, to begin nesting in New England and Canada. Now is the time, before the new tree leaves obscure our vision, to take binoculars and hunt for a glimpse of the sapsuckers, one of our most unique winter visitors. But if you find one, will anyone really believe you saw a bird called a "yellow-bellied sapsucker"?

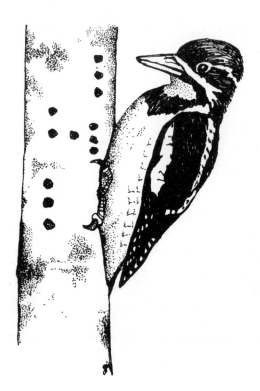

Second Week of March
White Beast

Face like a fox,
Ears like a bat,
Feet like a monkey,
Tail like a rat.

Now is the time of year when opossums are giving birth in the Southeast. The above verse was written about the seemingly conglomerate appearance of this puzzling animal. What an odd combination of parts the opossum is. Where does the opossum sit within the taxonomy of animals? To what family of beasts does it belong? It is a mammal, obviously. But what other mammal is it most closely related to? Is it akin to raccoons? to skunks? The Cajuns of Louisiana call the opossum the "rat du bois," or rat of the woods. But, despite some outward similarities, it is not even closely related to rats. When early colonists asked Native Americans what this unusual animal was, the Algonquians of the North called it "aposoum." Names change and shorten with usage over the ages, especially without written language. Aposoum is apparently what was left of the original words "waap-a'them wa," meaning merely "white beast." The Algonquians did not know what it was related to either.

The reason they did not know is that the opossum has no local relatives. Other species of opossums do exist, and these, of course, are our Virginia opossum's closest kin. Over a dozen species of opossums live in Central and South America. Opossums emigrated northward, along with armadillos and a few other tropical creatures, after the formation of the Panamanian land bridge, about ten million years ago. But what are these opossums related to? Stumped? Well, here's a clue: opossums are the only mammals in the New World that don't have belly buttons!

Doesn't help, huh? Okay, here's another clue, but this one will surely give it away. Opossums have pouches. Ding! That's right. It's easy to forget that the opossum is a marsupial. Like a kangaroo, the opossum gives birth to a mere embryo of a baby that must make the perilous crawl from the birth canal to the pouch on its own. (The opossum gestation period is only thirteen days!) Marsupial mammary glands are located in the pouch, and here the infant opossum, no bigger than a honeybee, finds a nipple and fastens its mouth to it for the next month of its life. Strange as it may seem, our own Virginia opossum is far more closely related to a kangaroo than to a raccoon. But how can this possibly be? They are so distant from one another.

When we ponder marsupials, we automatically think of Australia. But surprisingly, Australia was not the origin of marsupials. That is just where they have managed to survive, due to that continent's geographic isolation. Continents, we now know, drift. In fact, they

drift a lot. They are drifting at this very moment. Although tectonic drift is an unimaginably slow process, the continental plates have moved dramatically since the days when the first opossumlike creatures were raiding dinosaur nests.

Actually, it was in South America that the first marsupials evolved from their egg-laying ancestors. At one point, South America was part of a southern supercontinent, Gondwana, which included Africa, Antarctica, and Australia. Marsupials spread eastward across Gondwana all the way to Australia, which later broke away, never to rejoin with another continent. Therefore, marsupials, with the exception of a few primitive egg-laying mammals like the platypus, and animals brought by humans like the Dingo, continue to reign supreme as the only mammals native to Australia.

So what happened to all those other marsupials elsewhere? The invention of the belly button did them in. While marsupials ruled Gondwana, a different kind of mammal evolved in the northern continents: enter the placentals. Since that time, both South America and Africa have more than once collided with the northern continents and been overrun by placentals. Placentals, like ourselves and every other mammal in the northern hemisphere, nourish their unborn offspring through the umbilical cord, giving birth to much more developed young. This must give us an advantage over marsupials, because whenever the two groups have converged, the marsupial species have afterwards gone extinct in great numbers.

One possible explanation is that placentals evolved much higher intelligence. To compare the cranial cavities of an opossum and a raccoon of equal size, is a dramatic exercise. The raccoon's brain is about ten times as large. Though the opossum's head may appear as large or larger, his head is mostly bone and fat. The original "fat head," opossums have never been known for their smarts.

So how then, did opossums survive alone among the many marsupial species originally in South America? Well, sometimes it pays to be stupid. Opossums are what ecologists call "generalists." They don't specialize in exploiting any particular food source or habitat niche. They'll eat anything and live anywhere. Since they have no special talents or special needs, they can never dominate a resource, but neither are they very prone to extinction. Now they are thriving as scavengers in a world where our society creates hitherto unheard-of amounts of both waste and rapid change. It is likely that some generalists like the lowly opossum, despite their lack of intelligence, will inherit the earth we leave them. Opossums are a living fossil, little changed from the nest-raiders of dinosaur times. The white beast far predates us and will likely outlast us as well. In the long run, maybe intelligence isn't all it's cracked up to be.

Third Week of March
On Being a Part of the Food Chain

I t's biology class and the topic is the role of humans in the food chain. The teacher writes on the blackboard. "The grass gets its energy from the sun. The grass is eaten by cows. The cows are eaten by people. What eats people?" The class responds:

"Bears."

"No."

"Panthers."

"Nope."

"Alligators ... ?"

"Wrong again."

"What then?" they ask, exasperated.

"People are eaten by the mighty sand gnat," she replies.

Here in the Southeast, humans are indeed the prey of other creatures. But not the large fearsome predators that first come to mind. Sand gnats provide us with a nonlethal opportunity to feel what it is like to be in the middle of the food chain. Just think, the molecules that once made up the body fluid we lost to the sand gnat, are now being passed from predator to predator in the wild food pyramid around us.

Sand gnats that successfully feed on us lay their eggs in the muddy edges of the salt marsh. The wormlike young, themselves important predators of other minute creatures, are eaten by tiny killifish, which are eaten by larger fish, like sea bass, which in turn are eaten by bottle-nosed dolphins, etc. Who knows where your molecules might end up—in a giant right whale, or maybe in that kingfisher flying overhead.

Okay, enough of the romantic green notions. Who doesn't hate sand gnats? It seems they don't allow us even a day of mild spring weather to enjoy bug-free, these tiny grim reapers of springtime. Despite their size, they rule the outdoor lives of the earth's most advanced species. By this time of year, their reign in the Southeast is brutal and unchallenged.

These biting midges are so minute that in some parts they are called "no-see-ums." Yet they pack a wallop relative to their diminutive size. Looking under an electron microscope, one has little doubt about the origins of Hollywood monster designs. Sand gnats are all mouth, or rather, a mouth with wings! Armed with wings that can beat over a thousand beats per second and a barbed plow for a nose,

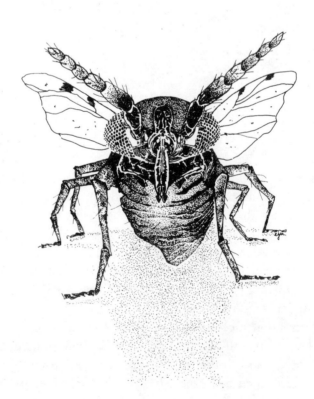

the little no-see-um has no trouble catching you and boring its proboscis into your skin. Unlike a mosquito, which is a delicate surgeon by comparison, the tiny sand gnat cannot dig deep enough to strike blood, but feeds off the fluids of punctured skin cells.

They seem to know just when to strike, too. You're under your car, both hands covered with grease, and that little bolt, the one you can barely reach, just ... won't ... budge. TORA, TORA, TORA! Maybe it's because we breathe more rapidly when extremely frustrated. Sand gnats track us by the carbon dioxide trail we create when breathing. So, to elude them, the trick is simple: just don't exhale!

No, really, there is only one strategy known to mankind that does the job. It must have been discovered by accident. I can only imagine the origin of this solution. Picture a backyard oyster roast on a fine Charleston spring evening. All is lovely: good friends feasting off the bounty of the salt marsh. Suddenly the breeze dies. It begins insidiously. It's barely noticeable at first, but you become aware of distinctly unpleasant sensations. The skin cells on your forehead feel like they are practicing volleyball player rotation. Prickly heat is creeping up the back of your neck. And then, suddenly you hear it, for just a brief second, the highest-pitched whine imaginable. A sand gnat has landed to begin feasting by your ear opening. Yikes. But you can't run for it because your neighbor is telling you about her daughter's latest problem stage. You try to pay sympathetic attention. Holding your drink in one hand, you nonchalantly rub the back of your neck. Your mind wanders a tortuous path. "So this is what it feels like to be a chew toy." It's getting unbearable. "I am a chew toy." Doesn't she even notice? Is she immune to this onslaught? "I am the chew toy of the gnat gods." The rest of the party is heading indoors, but she seems oblivious. Finally, your host saves you by stating the obvious. The neighbor lady is surprised. "Why, they're not bothering me at all," she says. She's not wearing repellent. The difference, they figure out later, is that she bathed in Avon Skin-So-Soft before the party.

Avon Skin-So-Soft is an insect repellent? Yes, where all other repellents failed, Avon accidentally created the world's only sand gnat repellent while developing their line of skin care products.

While most commercial insect repellents are far superior against mosquitoes and other insects, they have little effect on no-see-ums. Mixed half and half with water, this Avon bath oil effectively repels gnats. Some folks object to the oiliness of this concoction. Mike Ward, the "sociable hermit" who lives in the Ten Thousand Islands of the Florida Everglades recommends mixing equal parts of Skin-So-Soft, water, and rubbing alcohol. He says it cuts down on the oiliness, but still does the trick. Few people would have more experience with sand gnats than Mike. Avon does not promote Skin-So-Soft as a gnat-repellent, even dismissing this application as "southern folklore," but to a coastal-dwelling southerner, this folklore is for real!

Manly types may object to the fragrance it gives them. Even so, who would ever have guessed it. Now, in macho bait shops all across the Southeast, along with the rack of ball caps with things like "You can take my wife, but don't mess with my dog" written on them, between the Pabst Blue Ribbon and the blood-scented fishing lures, is a shelf of Avon bath oil spray, to keep your skin as soft as a baby's behind.

Fourth Week of March
Waxwing

Mulberry trees are in bloom throughout the Southeast. The elongate male flowers, or "catkins," are dangling from the leafless twig tips. I am reminded of this time a few years ago: I was relaxing under the bare mulberry tree in the small courtyard behind my house in historic Savannah, when I heard the familiar calls of a cedar waxwing flock overhead. Such a unique sound these small birds make—a quiet, drawn-out peeeeeep, at the highest pitch imaginable within the range of human hearing. At any given moment within a winter flock of waxwings, someone is always singing. The peeping of individuals overlaps, so that it sounds like a thin, continuous whispering from above.

A large flock of waxwings had settled into the mulberry tree overhead. To my surprise and delight, these small birds were greedily gobbling up the mulberry catkins as fast as they could. I knew that waxwings ate berries in winter, but I was surprised to see them eating flowers. And somehow they were singing with their mouths full, as they choked down these relatively large flowers. Some of these barely manageable flowers were being dropped when plucked, and I noticed then that a gentle rain of mulberry catkins was falling softly over the courtyard.

Like so many insect-eating birds that breed in the north country, waxwings change their diet in winter. Although some insectivores fly far enough south to spend the winter munching exotic tropical

insects, others, like waxwings, migrate only far enough to escape the worst of the north's winter weather. Waxwings are very gregarious and nomadic in winter. Since insect populations are low here in winter, the flocks wander about the South searching for berry-laden shrubs and trees. The whereabouts of a flock can never be predicted. But if you have a pyracantha bush in your yard, sooner or later, they will pay you a visit.

Waxwings are charmingly plump birds with a subtle handsomeness of fawn colors. Crested and black-masked, a waxwing could be mistaken for a washed-out cardinal who spent too much time in the sun. Waxwings are named for a peculiar dot of waxy material that grows at the back edge of each wing. Up close, the bright red spot stands out like a silk kerchief in the breast pocket of a formal suit. The function of this waxlike substance is unknown, but the fact that only birds two years of age or older possess it suggests that it may serve to indicate sexual maturity for the purpose of mate selection (not unlike a silk pocket kerchief, perhaps).

Waxwings represent a small family of songbirds native to mountains and cold reaches throughout the northern hemisphere. There are only three species in all of North America and Eurasia. The species that winters here, the cedar waxwing, is the southernmost of its kind, breeding even in the mountains of the Carolinas and north Georgia. They will be leaving the coastal plain soon to return to these lush places. In summer, they act like a different beast entirely. Pairing up for the nesting season, they snatch insects on the wing with dazzling forays over evergreen-lined mountain streams.

But from late fall to early spring, cedar waxwings are voracious fruit eaters. Few berry bushes escape these ravaging flocks. As berry eaters, however, waxwings are important seed dispersers for wild plants, providing a valuable service to shrubs and trees that bear such fruits precisely for this purpose. Owners of ornamental shrubbery, though, may be sad to see the bright orange berries of their pyracantha stripped away prematurely.

If such a shrub manages to keep its berries through the winter, however, a truly comical phenomenon of nature may occur this time of year. As pyracantha berries age beyond ripeness, their sugars begin to ferment with the warming sun of early spring. Waxwing flocks that choose to feast on such berries now may be in for a bird bacchanalia. The keen observer of nature may find dizzy waxwings lying on their backs beneath the pyracantha bush, their little bird feet straight up in the air, oblivious to the world around them. They may appear to be stone-dead, but given enough time to sleep it off, they will soon be on their way back to the north country for the summer, though their chosen path may waver a bit.

April

First Week of April
Return of the Native

Keen observers of nature will have noticed how much louder
the bird chorus is now each morning. This emphatic singing marks
the nesting activity of our local birds. Many of our nesting bird
species never do migrate south, but winter here as well, patiently
waiting for the sun to creep higher into the sky. Such permanent
residents, like blue jays and mourning doves, have already had there
nests built for quite a while now, since about early March. But most
of those species that do migrate south to warmer climes, usually the
insect-catcher types, are just now arriving in our midst, taking
advantage of the reappearance of our healthy "bug" population.
Among the many birds that have flown back to the Southeast Coast
in the last few weeks are the colorful warblers.

Generally, warblers are to the bird world what butterflies are to
the insects: among the most flamboyantly marked of their class.
Unfortunately, they are also among the smallest, and they rarely sit
still. One needs binoculars and persistence to see them, but the
reward is well worth it. Despite their name, few warbler species have
melodious songs. But one of our nesting warblers has a song that is,
if not beautiful, at least distinctive. In oak forests, listen now for the
zipperlike ascending trill of the parula warbler.

The tiny parula warbler is a brightly colored bird with a blue
back, white wing bars, yellow throat, and a characteristic black and
red necklace. Like most warblers, the parula flits actively about the

forest, hunting caterpillars and other insects. Called specifically the "northern parula" because he is the northernmost representative of his largely tropical genus, he has just returned from a winter visit to the haunts of his cousins in Central America and the islands of the Caribbean.

Northern parulas will soon be building their distinctive nests constructed almost entirely of Spanish moss. Spanish moss would seem to be the perfect nesting material, so it is a surprise that so few bird species utilize it. The northern parula often chooses her nest site within an existing beard of Spanish moss that requires few modifications. Its nest is often, therefore, indistinguishable from other clumps of the moss, making for a well-camouflaged nest with relatively little effort. The Southeast's abundance of live oaks draped with Spanish moss provides ample home sites for this, one of our most colorful nesting birds, a native recently returned.

Second Week of April
Out of a Mole Hill

He swims through the porous soil, employing a sort of sub-terranean breaststroke. Armed with strong claws reminiscent of the teeth on a backhoe scoop, his huge paddlelike forelimbs are oriented straight out to his sides. His streamlined body widens back evenly from his pointy nose, without indentation between head and shoulders. Pushing himself forward through the earth after each powerful stroke, he has been clocked at speeds of up to one foot a minute. Through an existing tunnel, he can move much faster.

Animals that spend most of their lives underground are termed "fossorial," and moles are our most fossorial mammal, rarely breaching the surface. Their bodies are highly specialized for their subterranean lifestyle. Moles have narrow, flexible waists for turning 180 degrees in a tunnel, usually by means of a somersault. Their short, velvety fur grows straight out so that they can move forward or backward without rubbing themselves against the grain. Though moles have well-developed hearing, their tiny ear holes are located under the fur to avoid clogging with dirt. Similarly, their eyes are merely light-sensitive pinpoints. The eyes of the most common species in our area, the eastern mole, are actually covered with a thin layer of translucent skin.

What are they digging for, these industrious moles? They are active night and day, throughout the year. Moles are predators of fossorial invertebrates, especially earthworms, which they track down

with their sensitive whiskers and acute sense of smell. Typically we notice the results of two different types of mole burrowing. The subsurface tunnels we see pushed up from under the sod, or through the soft forest floor loam, are either the result of recent hunting or a well-traveled highway from one place to another. The proverbial mole hill, a conical pile of loose dirt about six inches high without entrance, is the sign of deeper delving where the soil was excavated and carried to the surface, rather than just pushed upward as in a tunnel. Since not much prey lives far below the surface, these lower digs are generally for the purpose of creating a safe nesting area.

Moles are normally solitary creatures. But the female moles in the Southeast have recently given birth to their annual litter of two to six young. They are keeping them now in a deeper, grass-lined chamber, usually below a heavy log or stump. Bears, coyotes, and foxes will dig up mole nests, but digging them out is labor-intensive. Weasels and snakes will hunt moles in their tunnels, but they know their own subterranean pathways better than anyone. Moles are seldom caught. Therefore, moles have a much lower reproductive rate than most mammals their size. One small litter per year is enough to sustain the optimal population size.

Although they are cursed and trapped by manicured lawn owners for ripping through the sod, moles are an important part of our soil ecology. They aerate the soil. Their burrows allow rain to penetrate the earth and therefore erosion is diminished. Also, they are important predators of the grubs and insects that devour plant roots, so they can actually be a benefit to grass sod.

Third Week of April
The Rookery

Have you ever seen a heron nest? These large birds that frequent our salt marshes and wetlands would be hard to miss sitting on a nest. Yet few of us have ever witnessed such nesting activity. Most of our smaller birds rely on thick vegetation and camouflage to hide their nests from harm. Tall wading birds must employ a different strategy—safety in numbers. There is no sense in trying to hide when you are this big. So they nest in a large noisy colony, called a "rookery." The number of nests in a rookery may be as few as a dozen or counted in many hundreds.

Herons and egrets choose their communal nesting site very carefully. Favorite places are the tall trees of small islands or isolated patches in flooded forests, completely surrounded by water. And the water must be deep enough for alligators ... Did you say alligators? Why would these birds want alligators beneath their nesting colony? Their is a symbiotic relationship between wading birds and alligators. The main predator of these rookeries are infamous nest raiders, very adept at climbing trees: raccoons. To get to the rookery trees, the raccoon must swim through the water, not normally a difficult obstacle for such a water-lover. But that is where the alligators come in. The rookery is surrounded by a protective moat complete with hungry crocodilians. In return for guarding the rookery, the alligator feeds off the many fish attracted to the enriched water beneath

the nests, the occasional nestling that leaves the nest prematurely, and, of course, any raccoon foolish enough to attempt a raid.

A visit to one of these rookeries is an unforgettable experience. The visitor must be quiet and very careful not to disturb the birds at all. Some of the species that nest in such rookeries are endangered, like the wood stork. Although there are exceptions, the rookeries tend to be in remote places, away from human disturbance. And, of course, there are the alligators, who usually avoid anyone much larger than a raccoon, but have been known, on rare occasions, to kill people. But say you are undeterred by all this, and really want to see a rookery.

You rise with the sun on a clear April morning. You have packed the car the night before, and you drive to where the road ends. You hike through the dimly lit forest. The oaks give way to cypresses, their fluted trunks and gnomic knees rising from the increasingly soggy ground. You reach the edge of the swamp water. You put on your chest waders and proceed, slogging through the dark water as it deepens to envelop your waist. The baritone call of bullfrogs is like the chanting of cloistered monks. Mist rises from the black water, like steam off well-steeped tea.

The exact location of the rookery is uncertain, so you take your bearings from the sound of it, a distant murmuring from the depths of the swamp. A floating carpet of duckweed covers the water's surface now. Your path through the vibrant green mat is quickly and quietly reclaimed by the duckweed. It closes behind you like the Red Sea after Moses. Only the swamp will know which way you went. You are at the mercy of the swamp now, an uninvited visitor exploring its secret heart.

It is impossible to see the bottom through the black water. You feel for footing blindly, probing each step with your rubber-clad toes. The slick mud gives way to spongy peat, and the peat tries to pull your waders off your chest. Your feet stumble on cypress knees and sunken dead branches, and other slippery things unidentified. You try not to think too much about what those things may be.

The cacophony of the rookery grows louder. You glimpse patches of bright white plumage through the tall cypress trunks.

The light brightens as you step into the edge of the rookery. The trees are nearly bare, due to the constant activity of large birds on their limbs. Parents jockey for position on favored branches above the nests. Nestlings rock back and forth in the sloppy stick nests, grunting in unison, every nest with a varying cadence and pitch. Each nest contains young of different ages and species. Up high, a great egret is gently turning her eggs with her long beak. Below, a pair of snowy egrets are changing the guard, their long courtship plumes spread wide. To your left, a nest full of tricolor heron chicks, with down-tufted faces only a mother could love, wave their absurdly long bills agape, begging for regurgitated fish bits.

The hubbub of noise and activity is overwhelming. Everywhere are floating feathers and guano, like spilled whitewash. You find a cypress log to sit upon. You stare transfixed for a long time. You have entered a different world, a different age. Your former life seems far away and long ago. You become one with the scene; a big, greenish bump on one of the many downed cypress trunks.

Then you hear it, a drone altogether alien. A high-flying airplane passes overhead. You resent the intrusion. But as the offending sound grows faint, the noise of the engine is gradually replaced by a somewhat similar rumble, much nearer. As if in reply to the things of man, from three different directions around you, bull alligators are bellowing their deep, sonorous mantra.

Well, you think, perhaps it's time to leave. They've been there all the time, of course, and nothing's happened, you reassure yourself. As you slog your way out through the mysterious shapes below the water's dark surface, you try to concentrate on how much bigger you are, really, than a raccoon.

Fourth Week of April
Frog Orgy

With all the rain the Southeast receives this time of year, yet another spring rite is upon us: the mating season of frogs. Frogs can be added to the list of the creatures who are serenading us nightly, now that the weather is warming. Toads, owls, chuck-will's-widows, and a few insect species have been at it for a while now. Like most creatures who vocalize (reader excluded, perhaps), frogs sing for the purpose of attracting potential mates when the time is right.

Many frog species spend their whole lives in ponds, swamps, or freshwater rivers. But tree frogs, as their name implies, live the majority of their lives not only out of the water, but up off the ground as well. As adults, their habitat is in shrubs, trees, and even on buildings, under the eaves of roofs or behind rain spouts. During the day they can be found asleep, clinging tightly to the underside of a large leaf or anyplace that is shaded. To enable themselves to climb trees and walls, or adhere upside-down to the bottoms of things, these two-inch frogs are equipped with amazing suction cups at the end of their toes.

Beginning in April, however, tree frogs are compelled to abandon their highfalutin haunts by the universal urge to breed. Male tree frogs gather by the score in the ephemeral ponds created by spring rains. What would be the inconsequential voice of a lone frog is amplified to an impressive din when so many males sing in chorus. The louder the chorus, the more males arrive to join in, and the

chorus grows louder, and so on and so on. If a pond chorus of a relatively smaller number of males can hear that they are being clearly outclassed by another nearby chorus, they will give up, forsake their pond, and unite with the louder chorus. "If you can't beat 'em, join 'em" is the tree frog motto.

Each species of frog sings a characteristic song quite different from that of other species. The green tree frog, with his handsome creamy-white lateral stripe, has a twangy song that is best transliterated as "meernk." Also listen for squirrel tree frogs, so named because their "song" is completely unmusical, resembling more the short bark of an angry gray squirrel. But when frogs congregate in great numbers in spring, the resulting blend of voices creates one of nature's greatest symphonies, the individual sounds of which are difficult to distinguish.

Of course, not only males are drawn to the symphony. That would defeat the purpose. The local females also hop to the loudest pond. Partners are quickly chosen, with little courtship or protocol. Literally hundreds of frogs can all be mating at once, even in a relatively small pond. Beneath each couple, eggs are laid and fertilized simultaneously. The next morning, the keen observer of nature may notice many, many small gelatinous masses of frog eggs as evidence of the great, raucous debauchery of the night before.

May

First Week of May
A Swift Courtship

Above every city in the Southeast, above all our houses now, look for chimney swifts flying overhead. Their rapid, batlike wing beat, their dark, cigar-shaped body, and crescent wings are distinctive. Like stunt aerialists on speed, they whirl and circle through the urban skies with incessant activity, from dawn to dusk. All the while, they produce the quintessential twitter of the bird world. Once you learn it, you will be aware of the chimney swifts every time you venture out your front door during the warmer months.

They literally fly all day long. They never perch like songbirds do. Since they thrive on flying insects, which they catch in midair, they have little cause to sit. Some ornithologists theorize that they even take naps on the wing, though this would be nearly impossible to prove. Chimney swifts couldn't perch if they wanted to, actually. Their unbirdlike feet resemble more those of a small mouse, with all four short toes pointing forward. They are unable to grasp anything with this highly specialized arrangement of the toes. However, with the sharp claws on these toes they cling to the walls inside your chimney at night, bracing themselves with spines on the end of their tail feathers.

If you do not have some sort of screening over the top of your chimney, you may soon be surprised by the sound of twittering emanating from your fireplace. These swifts not only roost in chimneys, but actually nest in them as well. They have an extraordinary

---

method of gathering nest materials. While buzzing the treetops, they snatch dead twigs in their mouths, never missing a wing beat! The nests themselves are even more unusual. It's fun to hold a mirror in your fireplace and watch them as they build their nests. To form and attach the half saucer-shaped nest high on your chimney wall, they glue the twigs together with their own glutinous saliva. In the Old World, there is a cousin who makes its nests without twigs, but completely out of a similar salivary secretion. Eurasians long ago discovered that this secretion was rich in protein. To this day, these people collect the nests from colonies of this related swift and melt them into a broth to make "bird's nest soup."

Our chimney swifts recently returned to us last month from their wintering ground in western Amazonia. Some of the swifts we see now may still be migrating northward, nabbing insects as they fly. In migration, chimney swifts can form great flocks, roosting at night in abandoned industrial chimneys and ventilation shafts. As dusk settles in, they stay close to the roosting site, circling more and more tightly around the chimney's aperture. Then, with the fall of darkness, hundreds of them will suddenly swirl, like flotsam in a whirlpool, down into the dark gape of the chimney.

Chimney swifts are a species of native wildlife that actually benefited from the results of Columbus's discovery. Originally, they nested in large hollow trees, which, though they are not nearly as common as they used to be, were never as abundant as chimneys are now. There are probably many more chimney swifts living today than there ever were in presettlement times. One indication of this likelihood is that chimney swifts are now much more abundant over urban areas than anywhere else.

Some chimney owners may be concerned about harming chimney swifts by using their fireplaces. Generally, the swifts are not here during the fireplace season, but fire building during a late spring cold snap should be avoided, unless you know your chimney top is screened over. Roosting adult birds could easily relocate, but once nesting begins, the young would perish. You may observe that nesting is already upon us by watching the behavior of swifts overhead during the day. You may witness a chimney swift courtship ritual called "V-ing." Two swifts will pair off from the rest and fly closely together. Then they will stop flapping and glide, one behind the other, both holding their wings up in a "V" position. When you see this, you are watching chimney swifts in love, a sure sign of May.

Second Week of May
The Rumbling of Dragons

S it quietly at the edge of the salt marsh at night. Or take an evening stroll around a lake. Better yet, paddle into a cypress swamp at dawn. Now that the nights have warmed, you just may be lucky enough to hear it: a sound like a rumbling snore echoing from the cave of a sleeping dragon. It is almost more felt than heard. It is so low-pitched, you feel the vibration in your chest.

Such is the call of the American alligator. That it sounds dragon-like is no surprise, since these last remnants of the archosaurs are the living thing most similar to the giant lizards that ruled the Jurassic Age. Now is the mating season of the huge reptiles that haunt our wetlands. It may sound like a snore, but alligators are never more awake and alert. With this bellow, they are attracting mates and staking claims on their territories. And they are willing to fight each other for their patch of swamp and the right to breed.

You hear stories about alligators eating their own young, but this is a popular misconception. Alligators do not prey on each other. There is one circumstance, however, when they will kill and eat other alligators. The vast majority of territorial disputes end when the smaller of the two swims away, and quickly. But when bull alligators do fight, it isn't just for show. The confrontation can be bloody. The loser, if he is lucky, may slink off merely deformed for the rest of his life. Otherwise, he may be killed. An alligator who dies in this manner is often ripped apart by the victor, and even swallowed ...

piece by piece. Once in the Everglades, I saw a ten-foot alligator with the head of a six-foot alligator in its mouth. Nothing else remained of the ill-fated challenger, and even the head was gone when I returned a short while later. It is understandable then, that alligators roam more now than in any other season.

The larger the alligator, the lower is the pitch of the bellow. This distinction alone prevents many territorial disputes. A smaller bull can know at a distance not to challenge another male whose bellow is deeper than his own. Both male and female alligators bellow, however, and since male alligators can grow much larger than females, this may lead to some confusion, perhaps.

A bellowing alligator is a sight to behold. The alligator arches his head and tail out of the water. With his mouth closed, the alligator fills its throat with air. The throat bulges outward. Then, just before the sound actually begins, the alligator's entire body vibrates. The water around the alligator splashes like water touched with a

tuning fork. Water dances off the bony ridges along the back, almost as if it's been sprayed upward. With the largest bulls, the effect is especially impressive.

When humans hear the bellowing of alligators, they cannot help but be moved. It awakens something primeval in the listener. Upon hearing the ancient call, there is a brief second, before reason takes over, when your response is to want to run and hide. But, fortunately for us, these toothsome creatures seldom prey on people. There is no doubt that they possess the equipment necessary to do so. Never approach an alligator too closely. Like any wild animal they will try to defend themselves if they feel cornered. Big alligators could easily kill a human the same way they do other large animals, like deer, which they do hunt: grab and drown. But, alligator attacks on humans are very rare. Nevertheless, deep within our ancestral memory lies the frightening experience of being hunted by something large and reptilian. Such are the imaginative origins of medieval mythology: great dragons devouring young maidens and malevolent musings rumbling from the gaping mouth of a dark cavern.

Third Week of May
Smitten by Love

You are walking down the street, minding your own business. You are thinking about what to get your father for his birthday or about the deadline on this afternoon's project at work, when suddenly, love smites you on the nose. You have collided with a lovebug, or rather, a pair, a very bonded pair, of lovebugs. They are everywhere this time of year—a constant reminder that it is spring and sex is happening all around us.

Lovebugs provide a new meaning to the advertising slogan "Fly United." You rarely see them alone. Connected posteriorly, they awkwardly fly about bumping into shrubs, walls, and even people. (Well, of course they fly awkwardly, not only are they having sex, but they are facing opposite directions! Even the best Top Gun pilots could not be expected to steer well under such circumstances.) Although the female, the larger of the two, clearly has her say about which way to go, upon closer examination there does appear to be some sort of coordinated effort between them. When crawling, the male clearly walks backwards, albeit he hasn't much choice, being half her size.

Lovebugs are appropriately named, because they are actively copulating most of their adult lives. But they are not truly bugs. The word "bug" has a scientific definition in zoology. Potato bugs and stink bugs are examples of true bugs, which are a bit more beetle-like, with wings that are form-fitted to their backs, overlapping

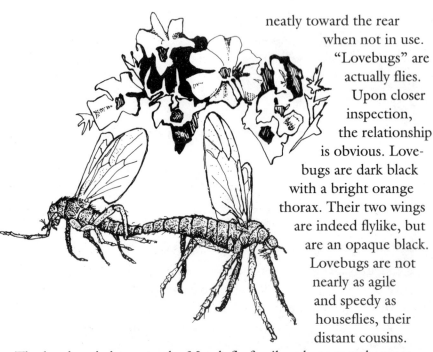

neatly toward the rear when not in use. "Lovebugs" are actually flies. Upon closer inspection, the relationship is obvious. Lovebugs are dark black with a bright orange thorax. Their two wings are indeed flylike, but are an opaque black. Lovebugs are not nearly as agile and speedy as houseflies, their distant cousins.

The lovebug belongs to the March fly family, whose members are known for their clumsy flight (even when not actively copulating).

The family is named after a similar fly that is similarly abundant at a certain season of the year (namely March). Lovebugs are abundant in the coastal Southeast in May and September. They do not bite or sting us. (Except, perhaps, to "sting" us with the reminder that we, ourselves, might be missing out on an important spring ritual.) Lovebugs feed on flower nectar and pollen, even as they are mating. Eventually, the female will lay a few hundred eggs in loose soil around thick vegetation. Then she dies, her purpose fulfilled. Her partner has died before her. The life span of the adult lovebug is brief. The sole function of this winged stage of life is to find a mate and lay eggs in another promising patch of earth.

After hatching, the maggotlike larva (or "love child," it could be called) dines harmlessly on decaying plant matter in the soil. After many months of this lifestyle, the larva pupates, then emerges as an adult. (A lovebug's childhood is much longer than its adulthood.) The progeny of the present generation of adults will reach adulthood themselves in September. The young of the September batch will winter in the soil, then emerge next May as the lovebugs of Spring.

We often think of insects as pests, but they all, even the most obnoxious species, play a crucial ecological role. Who could find offense, though, with the amorous lovebug, careening haphazardly from flower, to brick wall (umph), to forehead (ugh), to flower? Well, frankly, no one ever did until we developed the startling habit of hurtling ourselves at high speeds down highways. Now lovebugs are considered a nuisance by car owners. During heavy years, auto grills can be turned black with the smashed bodies of these spring lovers, rudely and terminally interrupted.

Since they tend to fly close to the ground, lovebugs are an inevitable target for headlights and grillwork. Unless washed off soon, lovebug body fluids can actually damage your paint job. So auto grill covers are popular this time of year in the South, especially for long road trips. However, if you are without a grill cover and the lovebugs are especially numerous, but you don't want your car to be so smitten, travel is safest at night, or in the morning before about ten. Like so many young lovers, lovebugs disappear in the evening and tend to be out of bed late the next morning.

Fourth Week of May
Flying Nuns

*T*hey stand on their squat legs like elderly nuns smoking big, red cigars, all facing the same direction—into the wind. Their bright red beaks are so large relative to their black and white bodies that they must face the wind or become living weather vanes.

Black skimmers are remarkable birds. Few species are so specialized. They earn their name from their unique feeding style. With wings held high, they fly low over the surface of the water, keeping the tip of the lower half of their open bill in contact with the surface. This lower mandible of the bill is shaped like a knife on edge, so it cuts smoothly through the water. Skimmers are the only birds whose lower mandible is longer than the upper. Sensitive nerve endings in the lower tip allow the skimmer to react with lightning speed when contact is made with prey. In a split second, the head is lowered and the beak closes upon the unsuspecting victim. The skimmer hunts the many tiny fish that cause those familiar raindrop patterns when they are feeding at the water's surface. Shrimp and other crustaceans are also taken. Like many creatures, black skimmers are crepuscular, so the best time to see them in action is early or late in the day. (Crepuscular animals are neither nocturnal nor diurnal, but active at dawn and dusk.)

This is the time of year when the black skimmers nest in the open sand of spits and wild beaches above the high tide line. On such exposed ground, the nesting birds can easily detect the approach of a predator. For such instances, the skimmers have a standard operating procedure. An unsuspecting beachcomber who stumbles upon a nesting colony will witness firsthand the daunting effectiveness of their defense strategy. The skimmers rise from the ground in attack squadrons. The first wave is usually dominated by females. They dive upon the intruder like flying fillet knives, swooping low as if to scalp an enemy. During the preliminary assault, another battalion rises to the air preparing to dive, while the last third waits in reserve. The initial wave returns to the ground while the reserves take flight, just as the second wing is commencing their offensive, so that at any one time, the nests are covered and the hapless human is under constant harassment by small, battle-crazed flying nuns. There are better places to beachcomb.

The nesting colonies usually include other bird species, especially terns, who are the skimmer family's closest relatives. The pale gray terns have a similar body shape until it comes to that unique skimmer bill. With their small beaks, the terns fish by plunging headfirst into the water, like a kingfisher. Somewhere along the line, long ages ago, a ternlike bird apparently developed the peculiar methodology of skimming for fish. Today, there are three species of skimmers in the world, with one each in Africa, India, and the Americas.

By feeding low over the water, skimmers are able to take advantage of a flight phenomenon that aviators call the "ground effect." Flying close to a flat surface reduces drag on the wings. An overloaded airplane can sometimes fly long distances, even if it cannot lift far off the ground. You may have noticed other sea birds, like pelicans, utilizing the ground effect by flying low over the ocean. As you might imagine, however, the skimmer method of fishing is an art not easily mastered. It is one thing to fly low to the waves. It is quite another to do so while keeping the tip of your beak in the water. It is not unusual when watching young skimmers learning to fish to see one flip tail-over-teacups into the sea.

June

First Week of June
Screaming Banshee

You are walking along a road at night toward your car. The parking lot borders a dense, dark forest. You are a little spooked. Who knows what lurks within the deep wood. You fumble for your keys. Suddenly, from high up in the trees, "ScreeeeEEEEACH!"

"Yikes! What was that?!" It sounds like a banshee come for your mortal soul. You jump into the car, slam the door and drive off, glancing in the rearview mirror for the red glow of the hell beast in pursuit.

Now is the time of year when young great horned owls begin their unearthly screeching. The juvenile owls, hatched earlier this year, are already full-sized, with plumage almost identical to that of their parents. But their calls are so different as to be unrecognizable. You might spend hours bravely confronting your fears, wandering through the woods at night, attempting to home in on the source of this terrifying screech. You track it to the top of a tree at the edge of the forest. Your flashlight can't penetrate the thick foliage. You can only imagine what is up there: a hatchling pterodactyl, long abandoned, or a demonic griffin, its eyes glowing red with inner fire.

By comparison, the call of the tiny owl that is actually called the "screech owl" is but a quiet whistled trill. Few bird books mention this aspect of the restless juvenile stage that great horned owls go through. The only voice written about is the mellow hooting of the adults: "who, hoo-hoo-hoo, whooo-whooo," almost too low-

---

pitched to hear. Great horned owls are fiercely territorial. Perhaps the juvenile call is so distinctly different so as not to raise the ire of the local adults, while the young ones seek out a place of their own. Or maybe they are as yet unaccustomed to their own independence, crying out for the attention of the parents that have stopped feeding them. The juveniles do not sound happy at all.

The reason this year's hatchlings are already on their own is that great horned owls are the earliest of our nesting birds. Here in the Southeast, they lay their eggs in January. Even up north, they nest so early that parents can be seen incubating their eggs in the high nest under a blanket of snow! Why begin nesting in the middle of winter? They start so early, because these large owls never build their own nest. They use the nests of large hawks, like red-tailed hawks, or even bald eagles. Hawk nests are substantial structures. Hawks and eagles are happy to utilize the same nest year after year, adding to it with each nesting season. Great horned owls will move in to usurp a nest well before the hawks begin breeding. When this happens, the hawk will not fight over it. These owls are so large and fierce that it is easier to build another nest.

The great horned owl, by far our largest owl, belongs to the genus Bubo. Found throughout the world, members of this genus are referred to as the "eagle owls" because of their huge size. Their talons are large and powerful, with sharp claws the size of which you'd expect to see on a bear paw rather than a bird foot. Due to the disappearance of so many big predators around the world (wolves, lions, bears), eagle owls, including our great horned owl here in the Southeast, are often the top remaining predator in their habitat. They will prey on animals as large as raccoons. Having incredible night vision and hearing but a poor sense of smell, they are the chief enemy of skunks. Wild great horned owls often reek from their latest catch, but it appears not to bother them at all. They also commonly eat other smaller species of owls, like screech owls and barred owls.

Great horned owls like to hunt the edge of the forest. They may actually be more numerous now than in presettlement times, since we have chopped down the great forests of the Southeast and created so much more edge habitat. They seem content to roost in small wood-lots during the day and hunt around human habitations at night.

All eagle owls have two "ear" tufts atop their heads. (The actual ears of owls are located further down the side of the face, below the level of the eyes, merely two large holes beneath the feathers.) Our great horned owl is named for these tufts, which indeed resemble the feathery equivalent of two horns, giving the bird a rather diabolical demeanor. This may in fact be the purpose of the tufts, to make the owl appear taller and more fearsome to its competitors, and perhaps to us as well. When your flashlight finally does find the source of the banshee scream, the appearance of the creature responsible seems very appropriate. Beneath the two devilish horns are a pair of big yellow eyes casting the light of your flashlight back down at you.

Second Week of June
Cuckoo Bird

C u-koo, cu-koo, cu-koo." No, it's not three o'clock. There really are such birds as cuckoos. Would you be surprised to learn that we have real live cuckoo birds residing right here in the Southeast? For most of us, the word "cuckoo" invariably evokes merely the wooden figurine in a Swiss clock. Or at best, cuckoos are perceived as a strictly European species—a bird of the Black Forest perhaps, whose call inspired the cuckoo clock. Actually, however, members of the cuckoo family are found throughout the world's tropical and temperate regions, including the southeastern United States.

Few cuckoo species sound just like a cuckoo clock—the sound of which is indeed the call of the European cuckoo that gave the family its name. But most cuckoo species do have similar calls, many of which are less like "cu-koo" than just a plain "coo" reminiscent of doves, to which the cuckoo family is most closely related. The most famous member of the cuckoo clan in our country is one of its least typical species: the roadrunner. The popular roadrunner of the West is just an overgrown cuckoo, who prefers running to flying.

Only one species of cuckoo actually nests in the Southeast—the yellow-billed cuckoo, a bird about the size of a blue jay. Another species, the black-billed cuckoo, passes through in spring and fall, nesting further north. Both species winter in South America. Being among the latest of migrants, they have only recently arrived in the

Southeast to set up housekeeping for the summer.

The two types greatly resemble one another, with a size, shape, and diet not unlike their better-known European counterpart. Cuckoos prey on insects, especially caterpillars. (Roadrunners, being so large, will eat bigger creatures, even lizards.) The specialty of our cuckoos is the ability to consume fuzzy and hairy caterpillars that make most other birds gag. Cuckoos have a unique crop above their stomach that strips off the irritating hairs of these caterpillars. After swallowing a number of caterpillars, a cuckoo will regurgitate a pellet of compacted caterpillar hair, similar to a small owl pellet or a lint ball from the dryer. This trait allows our two cuckoo species to be the chief vertebrate predators of tent caterpillars—the scourge of eastern trees. Because cuckoos wait for the peak of tent caterpillar activity to ensure sufficient nutrition for their nestlings, they are among the latest arrivals and nesters each spring.

In the Southeast, the yellow-billed cuckoo is also known as the "rain crow," for its habit of singing before storms. Though it may be the period of high humidity preceding and following rain showers that provokes them to song, quite likely their singing is due to the darkening skies, which remind them of early dawn, a time of day when all birds concentrate on reestablishing their territories most vociferously. Thus, in these parts, the call of the yellow-billed cuckoo is considered a harbinger of storm. The rain crow's call is loud and unique, even among other cuckoo species. It is among the most distinctive bird calls of our area: "ka-ka-ka-ka-ka-ka-ka-ka-

ka-kow-kow-kow—kowlp—kowlp—kowlup," beginning very rapidly and slowing toward the end.

The most notable and notorious behavior exhibited by many of the cuckoo species is quite the family scandal. European cuckoos never build nests. They don't use tree cavities, or old nests, either. In fact, these shameless libertines do not nest at all. The female European cuckoo lays its eggs in the nests of other birds! Can you imagine? Carefully casing out the local nests of warblers, wagtails, and other European bird species, she bides her time until the owners are away, flies quickly to the nest, quietly pushes out one of the eggs, and lays one of her own. Returning to the nest, the rightful owners usually do not recognize the new egg as different. The cuckoo egg hatches more quickly than the eggs of the legitimate heirs. And the young cuckoo develops rapidly, dominating the nest and hogging the food brought to it by parents that are run ragged trying to satisfy the hunger of a nestling often larger than they are. How cuckoos grow up to realize that they are cuckoos, as opposed to members of their foster parents' species, is a mystery. A European cuckoo never knows his real mother.

Due to this seemingly indecent behavioral trait of the female of this species, the call of the cuckoo in Europe carries quite a different foreboding to the listener. Instead of asking "Is it going to rain?" the call of the European cuckoo brings another question to mind: "It's early morning, where is your wife?!" This image of the cuckoo's apparent infidelity burdened the mind of many an English-man, leading to the origin of a Middle English word rarely heard now outside of Shakespearean productions: "cuckold." The husband of an adulteress was called a cuckold, meaning a man whose wife lays her eggs in the nest of another.

By comparison, our North American cuckoos are paragons of virtue. They build their own nests of twigs, leaves, and pine needles, carefully hidden in shrubs. And they always lay their eggs in their own nests, well ... at least, almost always. It seems that in years when tent caterpillars are especially abundant, some of our well-fed cuckoos will lay their eggs in other nests. Perhaps with so many juicy caterpillars to feast on, they just can't be bothered with parenthood.

Is such corruption the result of affluence? More likely, with all the extra nutrients they are consuming, the cuckoos can afford to produce more than the usual number of eggs, more than they themselves could possibly raise, so they take a risk and drop off their surplus offspring on the doorsteps of neighbors. Fortunately, on the rare occasions when our two cuckoo species exhibit this atavistic behavior, they almost always chose the other species of cuckoo as their victims. Where their nesting ranges overlap, black-billed cuckoos will lay their eggs in the nests of yellow-billed cuckoos and vice versa. What goes around comes around.

Third Week of June
Femme Fatale

Walk a little ways into an oak forest at night. Pick a cooler evening when the gnat gods are subdued. Turn off your flashlight. Wait about fifteen minutes for your eyes to adjust to the darkness.

Here and there on the forest floor, tiny yellow-green lights are glimmering. Slowly you approach a glowing spot. You carefully lower your face toward the source. Peering closely through the darkness, you can detect two pairs of lighted pinpoints atop a dry leaf. Lift the leaf and gently roll the creature into the palm of your hand. By cupping your palm, you form a reflective parabola with which to see the glowworm by its own light. A pair of luminous spots adorns each end of the flat caterpillar-like body, transforming this otherwise unlovely insect into a living, scintillant jewel.

"Glow little glowworm, glimmer, glimmer." Such a captivating phenomenon they are as to appear in our music and literature through the ages. Remember, in Thomas Hardy's *Return of the Native*, Wildeve's fateful dice game with the Reddleman, played in the darkening forest by the light of glowworms arranged in a makeshift arena. We have all heard of them. Though many of us have never seen one, glowworms are common enough this time of year. What are glowworms, though? And why do they glow anyway?

The answer to the second question is uncertain. Glowworms are predators of soft-bodied insects, slugs, and snails. It's possible that some of their prey are attracted to light. Or perhaps the answer to the first question is explanation enough: glowworms are young lightning bugs. They pupate and emerge as winged adults, much like a butterfly.

Walk now to the edge of the forest. If it is not too late in the evening, there we should see what glowworms grow into. Something stirs deep within us at the sight of a meadow full of fireflies, flashing against the dark backdrop of forest blackness. It can be dazzling, yet it is all so quiet. By all that is natural, there ought to be a sound produced by those flashes, a popping like flashbulbs, or at least a subtle whispering. But no, they are completely silent, thereby confirming to our superstitious souls that the whole scene is a work of magic: faeries cavorting in a midsummer night's dream.

An insect physiologist would explain that this seemingly magical phenomenon, called bioluminescence, is simply the result of combining a certain protein with a particular enzyme. Fireflies produce the appropriately named protein luciferin, and store it in the pale, translucent light-producing organ on the underside of their abdomens. When the enzyme luciferase is released into that organ, it reacts with the luciferin and produces energy in the form of 100 percent light. It may be simply a chemical reaction, but the production of light without heat as a byproduct is something human technology has yet to duplicate.

But why do they bother, these so-called fireflies? Lightning bugs produce light for the same reason katydids produce sound. They are attracting mates. In a great big world, tiny insects would have a hard time finding each other without some kind of system. The female firefly sits motionless on the ground waiting for the right signal. Males fly overhead, flashing intermittently. When the female sees the appropriate flash pattern above, she answers with an identical code.

We have many species of fireflies in the Southeast. Though they all look nearly identical, each species has a unique blink pattern. The number of flashes in a series, the length of each flash, the exact interval between blinks and series, the altitude and direction of flight while flashing—all are critical in the identification of a mate of the proper species.

A fun experiment is to take your camera and tripod to the edge of a meadow about an hour after dark on a moonless night. Get as close to the fireflies as possible. Leave the shutter open for a while. Unless you have a special light meter, you'll have to experiment with different exposure times. You'll also need a shutter release cable. The results are interesting. You'll see the different heights, patterns, and behaviors of many species, captured as flight paths on film. You can also attune yourself to the patterns with the naked eye, learning to identify different flash patterns. Attempt to follow an individual male. Count the number of flashes between longer pauses. Are the blinks instantaneous or prolonged? I have seen different species using codes from seven quick flashes to a single, prolonged glow lasting many seconds, reminiscent of a flying Tinkerbell.

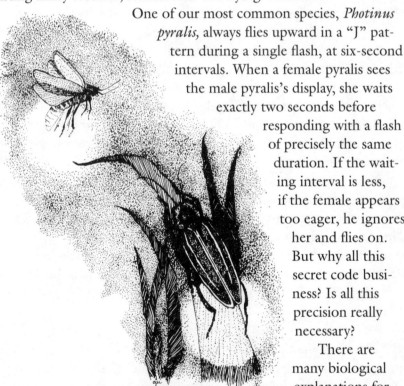

One of our most common species, *Photinus pyralis,* always flies upward in a "J" pattern during a single flash, at six-second intervals. When a female pyralis sees the male pyralis's display, she waits exactly two seconds before responding with a flash of precisely the same duration. If the waiting interval is less, if the female appears too eager, he ignores her and flies on. But why all this secret code business? Is all this precision really necessary?

There are many biological explanations for such species-specific courtship behavior, in general, but one reason for it among fireflies is quite colorful. Lightning bugs are neither bugs, flies, nor worms actually, but a type of soft-bodied beetle in the family Lampyridae (from the same Latin root word that gave us "lamp"). In the Southeast, there are two main genera of lightning bugs. The smaller *Photinus* fireflies eat nothing as adults and are therefore short-lived breeders. The aforementioned pyralis firefly is one of these. The other genus, the larger *Photuris* fireflies, are predatory as adults.

As different as even the various *Photinus* species' signals are from one another, you would expect that the larger *Photuris* fireflies, being from an entirely different genus, would have signals even more unlike the smaller species. But entomologists who have studied such things have been amazed to find that the large *Photuris* females are often mimicking, almost exactly, the signals of the small *Photinus* males flying overhead. Upon investigating an encounter, a small male was found to land near the larger unrelated female, and the female was studying him with intense interest. What happened next was completely unexpected. As the amorous male approached for mating, the female attacked him and began devouring him. Yikes! The *Photuris* females will mimic the signals of males of other species for the purpose of attracting and eating the would-be suitors! I've heard of hopeful males getting their signals crossed, but the consequences are not usually so extreme! Now we see why it pays to be a male firefly that watches his light patterns carefully. Beware the femme fatale!

Fourth Week of June
Tattletale

Walking quietly along the edge of the salt marsh, you are suddenly startled by a piercing cry: "wee-wilLET, wee-wilLET." A crow-sized bird rises from the grass, her distinctive black and white wing stripe flashing as she flies from you and lands thirty yards away. You move closer to see what she may be. She flies up again, repeating the process over and over each time you approach, until she has successfully lured you away from her ground nest which you so nearly stumbled onto earlier.

Unlike most of the sandpiper family members who are rather drab and difficult to distinguish, this bird is distinctively marked and easy to recognize. Named the willet because of its shrill call, this locally common coastal species has a broad white stripe the length of its black wing. The bright stripe is hidden when the wings are folded for the sake of camouflage, but it is prominently displayed in flight for the purpose of drawing predators from the nest and for claiming territory.

This time of year, when the willets are nesting on the high edge of our salt marshes, they are anything but shy. Presently, our willets are loudly proclaiming their territories. If you own marsh-front property, you have surely seen and heard them; their call is one of the dominant sounds of the salt marsh. If you are driving along a causeway toward one of our barrier islands, look for them perched on stumps and signposts along the road. While one parent lays low

and hidden with the downy chicks, the other displays itself prominently on driftwood snags and dunes to attract attention away from
the young.

Willet chicks, like all sandpiper babies, are precocial. This means
that, like chickens, the young, eyes open and covered with fluffy
feathers, are able to walk soon after hatching. Before the eggs hatch,
the parents share brooding responsibilities, changing the guard with
a bowing ritual. After the eggs hatch, the parents take turns escort-
ing the young about the salt marsh, teaching them to eat marine
worms and periwinkle snails and to probe with their long beaks into
holes for the abundant fiddler crabs there. The chicks learn to feed
themselves very quickly, but it is a few weeks before their flight
feathers develop enough for them to fly.

Unlike the smaller sandpiper species that only pass through the Southeast Coast in migration to return to their Arctic tundra breeding grounds, the willet can be seen in our local salt marshes throughout the year. Even during the winter, long after the chicks have matured and gone off to find their own territories, willets can be quite loud in response to intruders. They have earned the consternation of hunters stalking rails or wintering waterfowl by flying up and calling loudly, thereby alerting all possible targets to the presence of danger. For this reason, they are sometimes referred to as the tattletales of the salt marsh.

July

First Week of July
Loggerhead

A prehistoric ritual of summer has begun. Every night now, on the beaches of the Southeast, mysterious behemoths rise from the ocean depths, to be seen, like shadows in the starlight, by the naked eyes of landbound creatures. It is the nesting season of loggerhead sea turtles.

Few of us are in the habit of quietly walking the beaches of wild barrier islands in the middle of the night. But if you were a volunteer with one of the many turtle projects coordinated by the government all along our coast, this is what you would eventually witness.

All is quiet, but for the soothing sound of the surf. The beach is dimly lit by starlight. You carry your flashlight loosely at the end of your dangling arm. The flashlight is off. You won't use it much. Your eyes adjusted to the dark, you scan the surf zone. Walking steadily, you search the sand for the telltale trail of turtle activity, like tracks left by a tank tread, moving toward the dunes.

You've been walking for well over an hour. You're tired and your feet are already sore. The hard sand beats up at your soles with each step. The surf sings the song of sleep to your receptive mind. Then you see it. A dark mound cresting from the waves—a smooth boulder where no rock should be. You fall behind a driftwood log and peer carefully over the top. You must be very quiet now and patient, very patient. Any disturbance, any sign of danger, will send her back to the safety of the ocean. With the last push of the incoming surge, the glistening shell comes to a halt. There will be no more help from the surf's currents now. The rest is up to her.

Flippers designed for finer work, steering and propelling her through the buoyant ether of ocean, now press awkwardly for a purchase on the hard beach surface. "Scrip, shuffff, hiss … " Move flippers forward. Pull. The plastron rubs roughly over the sand. Breathe. Rest. To a being unused to the effects of gravity, even breathing is difficult. The unyielding earth pushes from below. Her carapace has become a heavy weight bearing down on her lungs. Each breath is a gasp. Each foot of progress requires the effort of Atlas. She is like a fallen angel doomed for a time to suffer the earthly conditions of mere mortals. She is a mother on a mission, risking death away from her deep sanctuary, for the sake of unformed young.

Eventually she disappears into the small dunes at the top of the beach. She has her own agenda and must not be disturbed. Eventually, she chooses just the right spot, above the high-tide line. She begins to dig. Bracing herself with her front flippers, she digs a hole she never actually sees. Alternating between her rear flippers, she scoops sand with a unique drilling motion she doesn't employ for any other task. So much that she is doing now is foreign to her, yet remotely familiar. If she is a first-time mother, she is acting on pure instinct. She never knew her own mother. She hasn't been out of the water, since her brief race to the ocean after hatching so many years ago. Yet the act of crawling on land must hearken to some deep ancestral memory of ancient terrestrial ancestors.

When finished, the excavation is the shape of an inverted light bulb, about two feet deep. As she begins to drop her eggs into the hole, she goes into a trancelike state. You could approach her at this point. A marching band on the beach could not disturb her now. She will lay all the eggs she has inside her, usually over a hundred, even if raccoons are there gobbling up each egg as it drops.

Raccoons are the chief predator of turtle eggs, and few nests remain unplundered the very first night. With their near-bionic noses, raccoons can sniff out a turtle nest, even if they miss the nesting activity. In the past, the very few nests that escaped predation

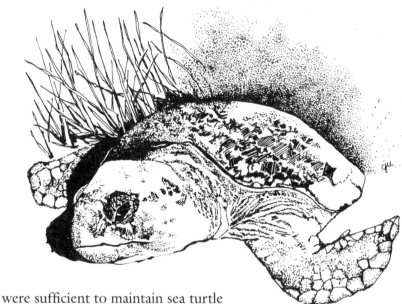

were sufficient to maintain sea turtle
populations. But now the situation is desperate.
There are just too few loggerheads left, and there is no shortage
of raccoons. The job of most turtle project volunteers is to beat the
raccoons to the nest, and move the eggs to a raccoon-proof exclo-
sure, thereby maximizing sea turtle nesting success.

A nesting loggerhead is a sight to behold—this huge, mysterious
animal out of the secret depths of the ocean, right before your eyes.
Her face is ancient. You feel like you are watching the last of a
dinosaur species, long thought extinct. It is a moving experience.
Around a nesting sea turtle, there is a quiet mood of sanctity befit-
ting the miracle of new life.

When she is finished laying, she buries the nest, disguising the
location as best she can by flipping sand in all directions to confuse
would-be nest predators. She crawls back to the ocean, disappearing
into the welcoming surf and leaving the world of dry land and
humankind for another two years. Scientists know surprisingly little
about the life history of sea turtles. Though they are large animals,
they range so widely through the ocean that they are nearly impossible to study in the wild. It is nigh impossible to actually watch their

behavior, even if you use scuba gear. They fly through the water using their powerful flippers. You can't keep up and you are soon out of air. Biologists can draw few conclusions about the species from observing nesting behavior. It would be like alien scientists trying to figure out what humans are like by observing only women in labor.

Sea turtles are an endangered species and therefore protected by law. It is best not to search for nesting sea turtles unless you are part of an official turtle project. It is too easy to disturb the females before they lay. A disturbed turtle will return to the ocean prematurely, and if she is repeatedly unsuccessful, she will dump the eggs to perish on the ocean floor.

Once sea turtle eggs and meat were relished by coastal southerners. But now there are too few left, and consuming sea turtles or their eggs, or even disturbing them in any way, is strictly illegal, with stiff penalties and imprisonment for perpetrators. In addition to being overhunted in the past, sea turtles have lost much of their nesting habitat due to the development of coastal islands like Hilton Head, Tybee, and almost all the barrier islands of Florida. Loggerheads need beaches with healthy dunes, and lights confuse and frighten them. If you own property near the beach, leave your outdoor lighting off May through September. With the turtle projects in place and the preservation of islands like Wassaw and Cumberland, we may yet undo the harm we've done and prevent the extinction of this magnificent creature.

Second Week of July
Rara Avis

*L*ike the columns of an ancient Greek temple whose roof has long since disappeared, the trunks of large pines surround you. Despite the fact that you are walking through an old forest, the sun is shining hot on your shoulders, the bright light barely diffused by the sparse needle-bearing crowns above. The tall pines rule here. No other trees are permitted. There are no shrubs or low branches in this forest. Through the widely separated pine trunks, you can see for hundreds of yards around you. The wire grass, growing thickly on the forest floor, brushes across your pant legs as you walk. Huge foot-long pine cones crunch under foot. In this rare remnant of ancient pine forest, you are scanning the tree trunks about forty feet up. It is midsummer, and you are searching for nesting signs of the Southeast's most endangered bird species.

Finally, you see a portion of the thickly armored pine bark that has been stripped away, leaving a patch of bare wood about a foot square. Yellow-white pine sap is oozing and drying in long ropy drips from the wound. What vandal has been at work high up in these stately trees? In the middle of the bare patch, surrounded by sticky pine tar, is a perfectly round woodpecker hole. You are thrilled because you know you have found it. The sure sign, it is unmistakable. You have found a nest hole of the rare red-cockaded woodpecker.

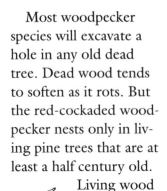

Most woodpecker species will excavate a hole in any old dead tree. Dead wood tends to soften as it rots. But the red-cockaded woodpecker nests only in living pine trees that are at least a half century old. Living wood is difficult to drill through with merely a bird beak, no matter how sharp and sturdy. That is why the red-cockaded woodpecker chooses only the oldest pines. Aged pines usually become infected with a fungus called red heart. It softens the dense heartwood, making excavation easier. The red-cockaded may peck a few old trees before finding one that is diseased. Apparently, they have no way of determining which trees are afflicted without beginning an excavation.

But why nest in living trees in the first place? It must have something to do with the red-cockaded's behavior of drilling small, sap-producing wells all around their holes. Dead trees do not bleed. But why make such a sappy mess of the nest entrance anyway? The pine tar is perhaps a defense to keep other species out of their holes. Woodpecker holes are a valuable commodity. Many species, especially squirrels and other kinds of birds, will nest only in cavities even though they cannot bore their own. They will sometimes bully woodpeckers out of their holes and usurp them. But the sticky sap does not appear to discourage these pirates much. Pine tar can be groomed off of fur and feathers.

Perhaps it is to discourage predators from entering the nest. Snakes will raid bird nests, but could a snake climb right up the straight limbless trunk of these old pines? Well, most could not, but there is one kind of snake, the rat snake, that is a tree climber extraordinaire. Rat snakes perform what looks like a magic trick when they climb straight up these pine trees. With very little twisting or turning, the rat snake uses its belly scales to grip the rough textured pine bark. They remain straight as a stick and climb faster than one would believe possible. Rat snakes are voracious and efficient nest robbers in the piney woods.

Field experiments have proven that these snakes avoid pine tar. Using their bellies for locomotion and with no way to groom themselves, a glob of sticky pine tar on their scales can lead to a world of problems. What's more, pine tar has been observed to be very irritating to snakeskin. A serious case can even be fatal. Needless to say, they avoid it, and we thus have the answer to our riddle. While other birds in the pine forest, even other species of woodpeckers, fall prey to the marauding rat snake, the well-tended red-cockaded woodpecker nest is protected.

So why is it so rare then, this little woodpecker? Red-cockaded woodpeckers were probably one of the Southeast's most common birds until a few centuries ago. Their habitat, the longleaf pine community, was the most abundant forest type of the southeast coastal plain. These unique forests, which were dominated by a species of pine whose needles are over a foot long and whose stately trunks were spaced widely enough to allow for unhindered wagon traffic, covered countless millions of acres, from Alabama to Virginia. Little change occurred in these vast forests due to the pines' unusual resistance to regular fires. Red-cockaded woodpecker populations, therefore, were always fairly stable. Reproductive rates were low to ensure against overpopulation. In fact, unlike other species, red-cockaded sons will generally wait a couple years before breeding themselves in order to help their parents raise subsequent broods. But these days, their slow population growth rate is to their disadvantage.

The same red heart that aids this species, now, in a sense, works against them. Loggers know that this fungus destroys valuable heart-pine. They also know that it doesn't strike these pines until they are over a half century old. Therefore, it is most profitable to rotate pine lumber at a safe age of less than fifty years. And so there is precious little red-cockaded woodpecker habitat left in the Southeast outside of the all-too-few protected areas.

Red-cockaded population levels have been steadily plummeting ever since record keeping of such things began. They have disappeared from almost all of their former range. One of the most frightening aspects of this dreadful trend is that, despite the fact that some former piney woods areas have been permitted to revert to the original habitat type, no one has ever documented the appearance of a new red-cockaded colony anywhere. Many, many have disappeared, but reappearance is, so far, unknown. It seems that, having been a denizen of the endless dominant habitat type for so many millennia, the red-cockaded has retained little ability to recolonize new areas.

The future of this endangered species looks bleak. How sad. We, who are the instigators of so much change on the planet, who seem, these days, to almost thrive on constant change—we share the earth with many species that are completely intolerant of rapid change. Is there no room for these delicate and beautiful species in the new world order? In the end, are we to be left with only the most adaptable of species; only the opossums, the pigeons, and the cockroaches? The rare and specialized members of ancient, undisturbed habitats must be permitted a place on this once-green planet, or they will disappear forever from the universe. And we, ourselves, may follow them.

Third Week of July
Did She or Didn't She?

Throughout July, with each passing morning, we are sadly hearing the closing refrains of this year's avian adagio of spring. But now, each evening, we listen to the crescendo of the seasonal sonata's next movement, and we know that deep summer is upon us. In these days of television and radio we rarely take the time to listen to nature's summer nocturne the way our grandparents did, sitting on the front porch at night, bathed in the sounds of the verdant season. When we do take the time, we are often reminded of our first camp out, or those long childhood summers when we still retained our sense of wonder about the world around us. The song of the katydid embodies the ripening promise of a summer evening.

Katydids are related to grasshoppers, but they live up in trees. Their diet consists entirely of tree leaves. If it is true that "you are what you eat," then katydids are living proof of it. Not only are they new-leaf green, but their large, flat wings are even leaf-shaped, complete with the branching, feathery venation a real leaf would have. These experts of mimicry look like a leaf with a head and antennae. Also called "long-horned grasshoppers," katydids have exceptionally long antennae.

As amazing as the appearance of our local species are, some tropical varieties of katydids are even more astounding. In rain forests, such as the Amazon basin, I have found katydids whose wings perfectly resemble leaves that have been partly eaten or attacked by molds, or even leaves that have died, curled, and turned brown. These katydids are so difficult to find among the thick rain forest foliage, that entomologists locate them by walking slowly through the forest at night, looking along the beams of their flashlights for the long, thread-thin antennae emerging out of leaf clumps. Predators have a very hard time finding these katydids. In the tropics, however, there is a family of bats that specialize in locating the katydids by tracking the insects' song to its source, using their ultrasensitive bat ears. Here in the Southeast, no such bats exist. Large songbirds, like blue jays and great crested flycatchers, with their sharp eyes, are able to detect the katydids if they move. But sitting still, as they usually do during daylight hours, katydids are perfectly camouflaged. We would never imagine how many of them there are all around us, were it not for their singing at night.

When one katydid begins to sing, any other male close enough to hear him will also begin. A chain reaction ensues, and soon the volume of the katydid chorus can be quite loud, sometimes almost deafening on the edge of a forest at night. Unlike many insect songsters, katydids do not sing in unison. Rather they alternate with their nearest neighbor, back and forth, in perfect unbroken rhythm. To the listener, the effect is stereophonic, giving the chorus a distinctive three-dimensional depth in the darkness.

One entomologist discovered inadvertently that he could induce a katydid outside his window to sing by tapping a three-syllable series on his typewriter. The katydid would answer his call with an identical retort. If the entomologist typed a two-syllable tap, the katydid answered with a two-syllable call. The man experimented successfully with two to four syllables, but could not convince the katydid to do more than four. Even a katydid has its limits.

The call is produced by rubbing the wings together. At the base of the left wing there is a series of small teeth called a "file." The right wing possesses a ridge called a "scraper." The file is rubbed over the scraper to produce the chirp. Much like with a bow over a violin, the player can move either the bow or the violin to produce the music. Also like a violin, beneath the file/scraper arrangement, there is a covered hollow space to produce resonance.

Why do insects sing? It comes as no surprise that this, like so many animal songs, is a love song. As with most singing insects, the eligible male sits still, while the receptive female searches. Even for a fellow insect, such a camouflaged creature is difficult enough to find by day, let alone at night. This is where the song comes in. She locates him by homing in on his song. Her eardrums are actually situated on her front legs! Being so widely spaced, her ears are able to pinpoint the exact location of her shy troubadour by using triangulation.

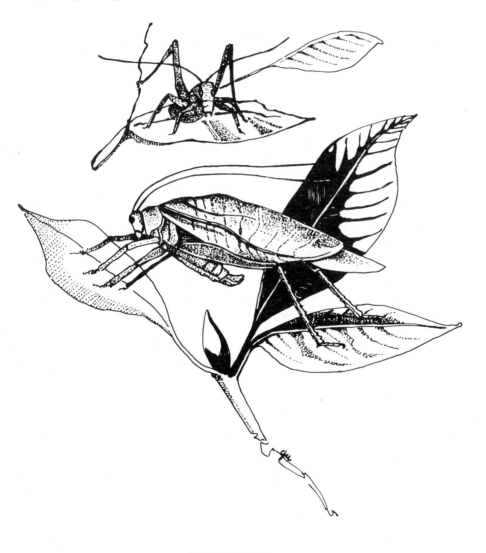

The female katydid is programmed to pick out just the right song, the song of her own species, from among the many species of night-singing insects that may be active at once. She does this not so much by the sound quality of the chirp or even the number of its syllables (a good thing too), but by the cadence of the chirps, or chirps per minute. This, however, varies with temperature. Insects are cold-blooded creatures whose metabolisms slow down as the air temperature cools. On a colder night, the male will chirp at slower intervals. Fortunately, the female's brain slows down at exactly the same rate as the male's performance. She hears more slowly when cold. So she always hears the katydid song at the exact same cadence, the distinctive cadence of her species, which allows her to recognize the voice of her kind.

We, however, can notice the difference that temperature makes on how often a katydid sings. In fact, the rate of deceleration is so regular that you can tell temperature by counting the chirps. The number of chirps in twenty seconds, plus fifty-four, equals the present air temperature in degrees Fahrenheit! But, first, you must find a solitary singer, not an easy task. Make sure it's a katydid, and not a cone-headed grasshopper or a tree cricket. Listen for the distinctive, usually three-syllable, song: "kay-tee-did."

If they are singing in the four-syllable mode, then it sounds less like they are saying "Katy did" and more like "Katy didn't." There seems to be some disagreement in the katydid community. Or maybe they just can't get their story straight about whether she did or did not. At any rate, it appears doubtful whether we shall ever know with certainty.

Fourth Week of July
Shark Attack

Jaws. As I snorkel across the deep, dark shipping channel between the Keys, all I can think about is that Jaws poster: the giant shark vertical in the water with its jagged, tooth-filled mouth agape, racing straight up toward the hapless blond. I dare not look down. I don't even want to put my mask in the water. Trying not to let my mind run away with the usual genre of highly imaginative fears it seems so capable of at times like these, I just keep my eyes trained on my goal, an island tern rookery in the Florida Keys. Snorkeling is a bit new to me.

Now, as I make my way through the shallows around the rookery, the water is so clouded by bird droppings, I imagine only shark faces looming at me, charging me through the gloom. "Most attacks occur in murky water," I remember the shark book stating. My heart is pounding. I can't climb up on land because I don't want to disturb the thousands of terns whose nests blanket the island. The only way back to land is across that deep, dark channel. Why am I doing this?!

The visibility is almost zero at times, with sudden clearings here and there. I round a chunk of dead coral and suddenly there I am, face to face with my nemesis. Evil, pale eyes in a face like the hood of a sports car. I freeze. When the shark sees me, he bolts off the bottom and away, his scimitar tail stirring up a cloud of white murk

in his wake. What am I doing here?! Will he circle around for the
kill, darting suddenly out of the milky water behind me? Probably
not, I try to convince myself. I'd seen it only briefly, but identified it
clearly as a normally harmless species, the nurse shark. Nevertheless,
as soon as my tachycardia subsides, I brave the ship channel again,
crawl up on the far beach, and collapse like a shipwreck survivor.

When asked about sharks, a marine biologist I worked with in
Belize once confided that she divided all sharks into two categories:
"nurse sharks" and "non-nurse sharks." It was the non-nurse sharks
that worried us.

Fortunately, nurse sharks are the species most commonly
encountered along the Southeast Coast. Despite the fact that they
can grow to be over ten feet long, nurse sharks don't even attack
many fish. They are bottom-feeders that prey on invertebrates like
crabs, clams, and sea snails. Nurse sharks have short, stout teeth for

crushing the shells of such crusty creatures. Their eyes are small and their vision is poor, but, like catfish and other bottom-feeders, their low mouths are flanked with sensitive barbels to aid in the location of prey on the dimly lit sea floor. In fact, they are so adapted to life on the ocean bottom that they can rotate their front fins to walk over the sand.

Nurse sharks are a primarily tropical species that seems to prefer warmer waters. The Carolinas represent the northern limit of their range, but as the water warms up this time of year, they will move farther up along the Atlantic coast, hence there are more nurse sharks in our waters now. One nurse shark habit that can give snorkelers or even beachcombers a fright is their tendency to congregate in shallow waters, especially at low tide. A small tide pool can contain half a dozen individuals lying together in a solid pile of shark flesh. (I can just hear it now: "Why, my Uncle Billy knew a man who accident'ly stepped into a nest o' sharks. By the time he made it to the other side of the tide pool, there was nothin' left of 'im but a pair o' hands.")

Because they are known to be docile, snorkelers will sometimes try to demonstrate their bravado by harassing nurse sharks. This is quite foolish, of course. It is never a good idea to molest wildlife, especially the toothsome varieties. A few nurse shark attacks have been documented, but all of them were provoked by ignorant people.

On that same snorkeling trip in the Florida Keys, I encountered a man who rather sheepishly related the events of his own encounter with a nurse shark earlier that day. He had had his eye on a single woman who was also vacationing on the island, and the bikini-clad beauty had accepted his invitation to go snorkeling with him. While swimming around the reef, they found a small nurse shark, only about a foot and a half long. He tried to impress her by picking up the shark. The frightened shark wriggled from his tentative grasp, swam frenetically around in a wide circle and bit the woman squarely on the left buttock. For a few frantic seconds the little shark held on and refused to relinquish its purchase. Fortunately, no flesh was actually removed, but a lasting shark bite impression was made.

She was so furious, she was speechless. She would have nothing further to do with the man. He was painfully embarrassed. But that very night, around the bonfire, I saw her going from person to person, animatedly recounting her story and showing her shark bite to all who cared to know about it—reveling in her newfound notoriety as a shark attack survivor.

August

First Week of August
Spider Stick

N<small>o</small> one wants to be first in line for long. Come summer, woodland trails on the Southeast Coast can become spiderweb alleys. Leading nature hikes as I have often done through the forests of the Southeast, I have learned after catching many face-fulls of spiderwebs to employ a "spider stick" this time of year. Held vertically at arm's length in front of my face, it adequately avoids the otherwise common consequence: spiderwebs in the hair and eyelashes. Worse, more than a few times I have turned my head while walking in order to answer a question, only to receive the fine sticky strands across my teeth when I resume facing forward.

The webs are difficult to see until you are right in front of them. Of course, they are designed to be that way; their invisibility is what makes them such effective insect traps. As unpleasant as this experience is for us, these webs and the spiders themselves are perfectly harmless to humans. But getting caught in a spiderweb is an insect's nightmare. The spiders are out there doing us a favor, actually. The many mosquitoes and biting flies that plague us during this season are common spider menu items.

But spiders have this problem: web building is time-consuming. It takes a lot of work. Plus, since the sticky threads are made of protein fibers produced by their own bodies, spiders expend a lot of energy on their creations. Along comes the blundering naturalist, deer buck, or even a blue jay, and a day's work, not to mention a lot

of valuable material, is wasted. If possible, try to avoid needlessly destroying a spiderweb. But it does happen naturally. Birds, in particular, since they fly at all levels through the forest and do not follow regular paths, are capable of accidentally destroying a lot of spiderwebs in the course of an active day. Needless to say, this is not a pleasant prospect for the birds, either.

The next time you have doused yourself with insect repellent and are out exploring the summer woodlands, examine a few of the spider orb webs you encounter (preferably before you walk through them). Eventually, you will find a web that deviates from the invisible orb that we think of as typical, by having a few visible designs woven into them. These thicker, white zigzag and ladder patterns puzzled zoologists for many years, and theories abounded as to why spiders would want to call attention to their own webs.

A few years ago, some enterprising arachnidologists (professional students of the spider world) conceived of an experiment to test a theory they had. They closely monitored the webs of a woodland spider species that does not create such visible designs in its web. They found that many of these webs were inadvertently being destroyed by flying birds, sometimes mere hours after completion. Then, the researchers crafted their own zigzag designs out of thinly cut white paper and placed these in a percentage of the orb webs in order to mimic the webs of the spider species that do this naturally. The artificially adorned webs consistently outlasted their unaltered counterparts, without significantly lowering insect catches.

It seems the local birds learn through experience to recognize the subtle designs as cues to alter their flight paths, while insects, being several orders of magnitude lower on the IQ scale, do not. Also, from a flying insect's perspective, the strange white zigzags hanging in midair seem easy enough to skirt between. And , of course, unlike you and me and the birds, an insect rarely gets a second chance to learn its lesson after a spiderweb encounter.

Second Week of August
Invasion of the Jellyfish

*T*hey're coming! They're coming! The days of August are here, and sooner or later they will come. They will be swept toward the shore along beaches throughout the Southeast, and suddenly the pursuits of boogie-boarding and body-surfing will become, at best, not much fun. Swimmers unfortunate enough to choose their day at the beach when jellyfish are in the surf in large numbers may find themselves immersed not in an ocean of cool, refreshing waves, but in a sea of pain.

The type of jellyfish that is commonly the late summer scourge of southern beaches is called, for obvious reasons, the "sea nettle." Although not as large or dangerous as some jellyfish species, the sea nettle can grow up to half a foot in diameter. It is a rather plain-looking jellyfish, its clear, bell-shaped body covered with small, warty bumps. Descending from the middle of the bell, four long, ruffled sashes make up the feeding arms. The beating of minute hairs on these feeding arms creates a current that carries food up to the mouth in the center of the bell's underside. The bottom margin of the bell is slightly scalloped. From each of the many clefts in the margin dangle the stinging tentacles, which can be up to sixteen feet long!

The stinging tentacles do not exist for the purpose of spoiling our summer vacation, of course. The sea nettle uses them to stun and capture small prey. Sea nettles eat small fish, plankton, and other smaller jellyfish, especially the little comb jellies. Insofar as moving laterally through the water, the sea nettle is at the mercy of ocean currents. But to maintain its proximity to the sunlit surface, where most of its food dwells, it can move upward, forcing water out of the bottom of the bell by means of contractile tissue around the scalloped margin.

When prey blunders into the sea nettle's path, it comes in contact with the tentacles. The tentacles are lined with amazing little stinging cells. Each olive-shaped stinging cell is loaded with a poison-tipped harpoon that lies coiled and waiting beneath a lid. A trigger hair near the muzzle of the cell trips open the lid when anything brushes against it. The harpoon penetrates the prey and injects its venom.

The stinging cells are not only useful for prey capture but also serve defensively. Although they are 95 percent water, jellyfish are eaten by some marine creatures. The giant ocean sunfish, itself a poor swimmer and drifter with the current, spends its life nibbling on jellyfish. The great leatherback sea turtle eats almost exclusively jellyfish … a lot of jellyfish.

The sea nettle has one of nature's stranger life cycles. Many animals, like frogs and tadpoles, for instance, go through stages in life that little resemble the adult form. This is especially true of most jellyfish. When congregated in the dense clusters of late summer, the adults release eggs and sperm into the water. After the impending death of the parents, the resulting progeny settle into a completely sedate existence for the winter, attached to the shallow ocean floor and looking much like tiny sea anemones. As spring approaches, tiny buds form at the top of these creatures, which break off to become minute jellyfish. By late summer the sea nettles have grown to full size just in time to create much consternation among beach enthusiasts.

Various remedies exist for jellyfish stings. The first step is to make sure there are no broken tentacle strands and unactivated sting cells remaining on your skin. First wash the site with salt water (fresh water will cause any remaining sting cells to fire) by waving the stung limb through the water or fanning the sting site underwater, rather than by touching the site. Then if you can see any broken tentacle pieces, remove them with a stick, pencil, or piece of shell, rather than your fingers.

But what do you do about the pain? Well, for a severe case of multiple stings or an allergic reaction, you should, of course, seek medical attention. For most cases, however, my favorite remedy is to soak the sting in water that is as hot as you can stand it. The pain miraculously disappears almost immediately. Unfortunately, soaking is often impractical depending on where you are (and where you've been stung!). Next best, though less effective, is to take some Adolf's meat tenderizer with you to the beach. Moisten the powder and apply it directly to the sting. Both the hot-water treatment and the enzymes in the meat tenderizer work on the same principle. They denature the proteins in the toxin, converting it to a harmless substance. Another way to achieve this is with ammonia.

"So," you say, "what if the hot soak is impractical and I don't just happen to have any Adolf's or ammonia with me?!" Well, I can't officially recommend this, but there may be an auxiliary first aid measure to be learned from the following encounter a friend of mine had in the Bahamas. You see, we all carry our own little source of ammonia with us where ever we go, though it may not always be readily obtainable. My friend had just been painfully stung while snorkeling a beautiful Bahamian reef. He hauled himself up onto the nearby beach, grimacing and pulling off his flippers. A seasoned Bahamian native noticing his distress, offered a local remedy: "Mon, ya have just da ting you need for dat," he said, and proceeded to recommend that my friend urinate on his own ankle. A seasoned traveler and naturalist, my friend knew better than to shun local remedies for local problems. It proved remarkably effective. But, like I said, I don't recommend this treatment—at least, not to strangers.

Third Week of August
Like Minks

Y ou are paddling quietly through the salt marsh. The only sound you make is the water dripping off your paddle on the upstroke. Boat-tailed grackles flap their panicky wings across the creek. Armies of fiddler crabs move in jerky unison up the mud banks exposed by low tide. A green heron, with slow, purposeful wing beats, cruises overhead, while diamondback terrapin heads emerge and quickly disappear into the brackish water around you. A marsh hen clacks loudly, completely hidden in the cordgrass, not ten feet from your port side.

If you paddle along marsh creeks regularly, these are the sights and sounds you have grown used to, grown to love. This is a world unknown to the roaring motorboaters who use the twisting creeks as shortcuts to fishing grounds or as a banking raceway in which to test their reaction times. But even the quiet paddler does not expect to see much wildlife of the furry variety. The salty marshes are a harsh world that few mammals can abide.

But, as you round a bend you are surprised to see a pair of beady mammalian eyes watching you curiously from the mud bank. The animal's rich fur is the color of milk chocolate. Its body proportions are all strange: short legs on a long, weasel-like torso. But it is many times larger than a weasel. You know it's a mink. You have seen them in the marsh before, but not so often that it isn't a thrilling moment still. You know it will be an all-too-brief moment as well.

You freeze and drift with your momentum. Were you in a motor boat, the mink would have been long gone before you rounded the bend. But now, the mink is curious. With quick, darting motions, it hides itself in the cordgrass, only to reemerge on the bank an instant later. Perhaps you are only a big piece of drift wood, you are so still. The small head tilts quickly upward, sniffing. The mink is not fooled for long. It smells danger and disappears in a blur of motion.

The many expanses and fingers of salt marsh that invade the Southeast Coast make ideal habitat for many species of water-loving wildlife. Most need fresh water and dry land to live on, but hunt actively in the salt marsh's rich organic system. The salt marsh edge that winds its way along the mainland is perfect for minks. They are quite common here, often denning in banks and bluffs near the marshes. They are excellent swimmers, paddling with their slightly webbed feet. But they are chiefly nocturnal, so, even if they were not so wary of us, we would rarely see them.

Renowned for their fierceness, their luxurious pelt and ... one other thing, minks are an animal that we all have heard of, even if we've never seen one or know very little about their lives in the wild. Most of our minks feed chiefly on small prey such as fish, rodents, and birds, so abundant in the marshes. But an occasional marsh rabbit is not above them. They are famous for being able to subdue prey larger than themselves, dispatching them with death bites to the back of the neck. Their elongated shape allows them to ferret out smaller prey in the protective nooks and crannies that exclude most larger predators. Like a snake, the mink can fit into a small rodent hole, then bring its considerably larger bulk to bear when the hunt is up. They eat small prey on the spot. They will drag same-size prey to their den, where it may be stored for later. But with larger prey, they will often gorge themselves and leave the rest, dining only on their favorite cuts. For this behavior they are scorned as vicious and wasteful, especially by chicken coop owners who have found their chickens slaughtered, but little eaten.

As for their pelts, minks are still trapped and skinned and their pelts traded or sold to fur companies, as they have been for the many millennia since humans arrived on this continent. Their wari-

ness is warranted. These days, however, the majority of furs used to make mink coats are from animals raised on commercial mink farms. (The many color varieties of mink fur are the result of selective breeding.) Yet humans are not their only enemy. Because of their small size, they are a midlevel predator, themselves prey to foxes, bobcats, and great horned owls.

Lastly, minks are known for their sexual vigor. Up there in that category with rabbits and a few other creatures, they are believed to engage in such activity frequently and for long periods at a time. Like so many of the traditional qualities we have assigned to different animals, this idea originated long ago, when people were much more aware of the unique behaviors of the other species with which we share the planet. Being predators with typically low population densities, however, minks must surrender the title for proliferation to rabbits and other small herbivores that reproduce rapidly. But when it comes to staying power in the sexual act itself, minks have earned their place in history.

The females of most mammal species ovulate at seasonal intervals wherein they become receptive to sexual activity. In the weasel family, to which the mink belongs, however, there are many species whose females, though aroused just at this time of year, ovulate only in response to actual sexual activity. For this purpose, sexual activity must be sustained long enough, and with sufficient vigor, to induce the desired response. Such a burden of performance would perhaps make the males of many species run and hide come the mating season. But not the virile mink, legendary for his prowess.

He has a secret, though. To assist in attaining such an enviable achievement, minks are among the lucky few mammal species whose males are naturally endowed with a special anatomical structure, called a baculum. The baculum is a bone that you will not find on the human skeleton. That many men have hired surgeons and paid great sums to duplicate this anatomical structure speaks to its usefulness. Surely many a Don Juan has wished that Mother Nature had been as generous with humans as she was with the mink.

This time of year the young minks, who were born in April, are following their mother all about, learning the tricks of the predatory business. By now, these kits, numbering four on average, are almost as big as their mother, but are filled with youthful friskiness, yelping and wrestling with each other continuously. With all this rambunctious racket, it's amazing that the mother is able to sneak up on anything at all.

Fourth Week of August
A Zebra Comes to Carolina

Hiking through a thick forest in the Everglades wilderness late one afternoon, I came upon the low limb of a tree that appeared to be shimmering with subtle iridescence. Upon closer inspection, I realized that I had found the overnight roost of some zebra longwing butterflies. I had heard that these unusual butterflies will gather together at night, forming a glossy black mass of wings streaked with creamy yellow lines, on the underside of a tree limb. Some of the individuals were still, while others were fluttering in, out, and around the mass.

Part of the magic of the zebra longwing is the way it uses its unusually narrow wings. It flies with a faster, shallow wing beat that gives its flight pattern less the appearance of a bounding flutter and more of a gliding shimmer. It moves along smoother paths and hovers easily, like a fairy delivering a secret message. As dusk fell on the zebras' roost, the enchanting sight was slowly obscured, but an unforgettable image was imprinted on my memory.

Though it can be found in Florida and south Georgia year-round, in South Carolina it is seen most often in late summer. At the northern limit of its range here in the Southeast, the zebra is not fond of cold weather. A bad winter or even a severe frost can kill off the most northerly individuals and knock their northern limit southwards. The family it belongs to, Heliconidae, is a primarily tropical family. The zebra is one of only a few representatives found north of the Mexican border.

Hiking through the rain forests of South America, I have seen many different species of this family. The longwings seem to be the most common family down there. But perhaps the emphasis should be on the word "seem." Because a longwing incorporates into its body the poisons of the particular plant the caterpillars eat (as do the monarch butterfly caterpillars), its coloration and shape are mimicked by other tropical butterfly species. A well-known mimic of our monarch, the viceroy butterfly, does the same thing. Bright colors in nature are often a warning to predators that the animal in question tastes bad. Young birds, through repeated negative reinforcement, learn early to avoid these brightly colored butterflies. If other butterflies look similar enough to the brightly colored longwings, they too will be avoided. And so, natural selection encourages this mimicry.

The relationships between insect species and the plants they eat can be very specific. Over the eons, as a given species of plant is munched on by insects, it evolves poisons in its leaves to discourage the marauders. This works, but because the process is a slow one, inevitably a few insect species meanwhile develop a resistance to the toxins, and a long-term relationship is created. As the plant species evolves chemical defenses, these herbivorous insects adapt until eventually they become the only species able to graze that kind of plant. This process is called coevolution. Often the insect evolves the ability to actually benefit from the plant poisons by incorporating them into its own shell, thereby making itself unpalatable to predators.

So it is with the longwings. Most longwing caterpillars, including the zebra, eat only the toxic leaves of the passionflower vine. Adult female longwings lay their eggs only on passionflower vines, usually on the tendrils, so that the caterpillars can begin feasting immediately after they hatch. The caterpillars are born hungry. They do not want to share their vine with anyone, so they will devour any other longwing caterpillars they encounter. Knowing this, the zebra female will not lay more than one egg at a time. Nor will she lay an egg on a vine where she sees another bright orange zebra egg has already been laid.

Here is where the passionflower vine has evolved a particularly devious defense. The next time you see a passionflower vine, look closely at the tendrils it uses to grasp and climb up trees. Particularly on the vines further south where longwings are more common, you may find, if you are diligent, a small orange nub along a tendril. "Aha," you may think, "I've found a longwing egg." Well, perhaps you have, but look again. Gently try to remove the orange bump from the tendril. Chances are good that it is part of the plant and not an egg at all. In the ongoing twists and turns of the coevolving fight between the passionflower and its nemesis, some vines have evolved random orange nubs on their tendrils to mimic longwing eggs, thereby discouraging females from choosing them as an egg-laying site! Nature is endlessly fascinating.

Look for zebra longwings near the tall sunflowers starting to bloom now. Like many other butterflies, they seem to prefer bright yellow and orange flowers as a nectar source. Mexican sunflowers, or other flowers that possess both yellow and orange coloration, are a guaranteed draw.

September

First Week of September
The Scorpion Under the Bed

"There's a scorpion under my bed!" The caller was a little frantic. Nature centers receive calls of this sort regularly. People just don't know where else to call when confronted with a predicament of the wildlife variety. The person who happened to pick up this particular call, however, was Ted, who had a special interest in such "creepy-crawlies" as insects and spiders. He advised the caller to remain calm, knowing that the only species of scorpions found in the southeastern region are small and relatively harmless. "No, this one's big," said the caller. There was a pause as she forced herself to look under the bed again. "Half a foot long! What should I do?"

Now Ted's curiosity was really piqued. "Surely her estimate is exaggerated by fear," he thought. He was from Missouri and had lived down here only a couple of years. Still, this was his specialty, and he knew there was no scorpion in these parts much more than an inch long. "Must be an escaped western species," he thought. He pictured it in his mind: fierce, gaping pinchers flanking its wide, spiderlike face, the barbed tail poised ominously over its huge, armored body. The entomologist in Ted would not allow him to stay in the office. Much to the woman's relief, he offered to come to her house and remove the dread creature from under her bed.

After wandering along unfamiliar streets for a while, Ted located the woman's home and was led directly to the offensive scorpion. Cautiously, he peered under the bed. He found a creature there all right, but to his complete surprise the animal was a lizard. It was clear from the anguished look on the lady's face, that this lizard was the "scorpion" to which she had been referring. Being a biologist and an educator, Ted felt compelled to correct her: this was no scorpion. She was not at all convinced. She now looked unsure of her rescuer. He managed to capture the lizard. Her suspicions about Ted's qualifications were now clearly confirmed. To her horror, he held the creature in his bare hands. "But they're poisonous! Watch out for the tail!" she exclaimed.

"They're perfectly harmless," Ted replied, somewhat defensively. But speaking of the tail that caused so much dread, where was it now? It was not on the lizard. He looked down. The bright blue tail lay on the bedroom floor, wriggling back and forth of its own volition. Holding the remainder of the lizard in his hand, Ted was not really surprised; it was an old lizardly trick. But the woman was horrified. Staring at the squirming member beside her bed, her face was a picture of revulsion. Ted picked up the tail as he walked out. She was visibly relieved. The threat was removed, the ordeal over. Ted, however, was very puzzled, both to hear this new usage of the word "scorpion" and to see such fear inspired by this little lizard species he knew so well.

The lizard in question is indeed harmless, at least to humans. It is a handsome animal; black with five yellow stripes down its back and sides. Its tail is very blue. Like most members of the skink family of lizards, its scales are so smooth and shiny that the lizard's dry skin looks slick, like a wet salamander. Although locally some folks call this type of lizard a "scorpion," biologists call it, not surprisingly, the five-lined skink.

The puzzling legend of its poisonous nature may actually have an easy explanation. The five-lined skink's tail is not poisonous in the same way a scorpion's is. It is, however, toxic in the way some mushrooms are: poisonous to eat. Fortunately, we are not in the habit of eating lizards, so this doesn't concern most of us. Cat owners, though, need to be aware of this obscure fact. Many folks have outdoor cats that stalk and eat small wild animals, including lizards. Some lizards, like the green "chameleon " so common in the Southeast, are safe enough. The five-lined skink, however, is not. Its flesh contains a neurotoxin that affects the nervous system. Domestic cats that eat these lizards typically develop difficulty with balance or suffer paralysis, and need veterinary care.

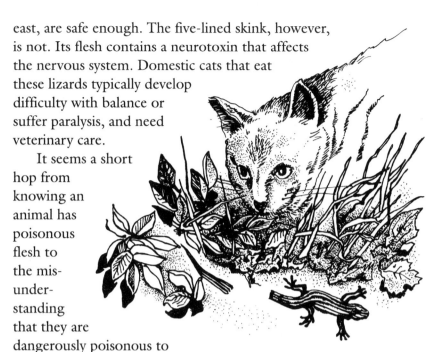

It seems a short hop from knowing an animal has poisonous flesh to the mis-under-standing that they are dangerously poisonous to passersby. Add the bright blue tail, and it seems not unreasonable to associate them with that most infamous of poiso-nous arthropods, the scorpion.

Even without the scorpion mythology, the bright blue tail has probably saved the life of many a five-lined skink. At the base of the skink's tail, there is a special cross-section of tissue that cuts through skin, muscle, and even bone. Two layers of cells interface here. Amazingly, the skink is able to instantaneously halt all blood supply to these two layers. When this happens, the two layers fall apart from one another. The tail then drops off and wiggles wildly. When spy-ing a skink, a predator naturally keys in on the bright blue of the tail, rather than the skink's head or body. By the time the predator pounces and discovers it has caught only the squirming tail, the skink has found refuge elsewhere. It will require many months for the skink to regenerate a new tail, but, obviously, it is well worth the expense. What's more, to some would-be predators like our pet cats, the only tidbit thcy do get is poisonous to them. Obviously, the skink's natural predators have evolved an immunity to the neurotoxic flesh, or skinks would have no predators and we'd be overrun by a plague of lizards.

Skinks are more active than most lizards. Rather than waiting in ambush, or carefully stalking, skinks often scare up their prey by scratching through the leaf litter on the forest floor. They prey primarily on insects, grubs, spiders, and earthworms.

Another unusual behavior of skinks is their motherly quality. Most reptiles lay their leathery eggs under a rotting log and then depart, never seeing the eggs again or even knowing their own progeny. The mother skink, however, stays coiled around her clutch of eggs throughout the two-month incubation period. Being "cold-blooded," she has no warmth to impart to the incubation process. The summer sun and the decay process in the rotting log provide that. But, since reptile eggs have softer, more permeable shells than bird eggs, they are very vulnerable to dehydration. The mother

skink monitors the humidity of her hatchery and voids fluid from her bladder over the eggs if they start to dry out. Also, she will ward off any smaller scavengers that would otherwise feast on the eggs. However, once they hatch, the young, tiny replicas of herself are on their own.

Having been laid in early June, our skink eggs have hatched out by this late in the summer. The hatchling five-lined skinks are roaming our woodlands now. They have a striking appearance. Like most reptiles, skinks are most colorfully marked when young, then gradually dull with age. The bodies of the juveniles are very glossy black with distinct striping. But it's the tail that is amazing. It is unbelievably blue—electric blue. Pigments for true blue are the rarest of colors in the natural world. The blue of blue jay feathers, for instance, is a structural color caused by the way sunlight is refracted by the microscopic structure of the feathers. These young skinks are the truest bluest wild animals of the Southeast.

Second Week of September
Fiddler on the Marsh

*L*ike strolling violinists with a surly attitude, the male fiddler crab holds his one hugely exaggerated claw tucked under his chin, as he feeds in the salt marsh mud. Their stout-hearted appearance and pugnacious character have won these tiny crabs an endearing place in our hearts. Certainly fiddler crabs are one of the most numerous animals in the salt marsh. Their population densities can measure over a million individuals per acre. From a little distance, they can appear as a migrating herd of wildebeests far below, moving in jerky unison over a mud-dark African plain.

In a sense, fiddler crabs really are little grazers, not unlike herd animals viewed from an airplane. They use their smaller claw (of which the females have two) to sift through the sandy marsh mud, gleaning plankton and detritus left by the most recent outgoing tide. As they feed, they stand still at intervals, scraping the surface layer toward themselves. Each time they move a bit further along to their next slurping station, they leave behind a tiny BB-sized "feeding ball" of sandy mud sucked clean of nutrients.

The home site of a fiddler crab colony is something to see. The ground is randomly perforated, looking like the results of five hundred ammunition rounds, of fifty different calibers, shot into the mud. The holes are flush with the surface, without walls or ledges. All around the burrows the ground is littered with feeding balls, as well as thousands of larger pea-sized pellets. These larger "excavation balls" radiating out from each burrow are rolled out by the fiddlers as they dig their homes. Each fiddler has its own burrow. Depending on the size of the crab, the hole's diameter can be as great as the width of a man's finger. Up to three feet long, the length of fiddler burrows in a given area will be surprisingly uniform, with the horizontal end chamber just low enough so that the burrow walls are kept moist by the tides.

That the humidity remains sufficiently high in the burrow is important to fiddlers, because unlike most crabs, which have gills, fiddlers possess a primitive kind of air-breathing lung. At the bases of a blue crab's legs, you would find the openings to the gills, called "dead man's fingers" by local crab meat connoisseurs. But at these joints, a fiddler crab has highly vascularized bronchial chambers that can draw oxygen from the air, if kept moist enough. On the other hand, with too much water, a fiddler can actually drown. As they are inundated by each high tide, some species of fiddlers prevent flooded burrows by stoppering up the entrance with a plug of mud, thereby sealing an air space within the burrow.

Among the most charming antics in the animal world is the "dance of the fiddlers." Although it is a stationary behavior, the male fiddlers perform a set series of movements very like barre exercises in ballet. Standing on tiptoes, with eye stalks at full mast, he executes his grande plié with a flourish. While deep knee-bending rhythmically, he draws his large claw across his face and, with a continuous sweeping motion, waves it into the air, like a port de bras. Some species return the claw downwards with an audible (if you are very close) thump on the ground. Each species has a different variation on the theme, and upon those uncommon edges where the microhabitats of all three of our species overlap, the resulting show of male vanity is a sight to behold.

This summertime dance is, of course, a courtship behavior. Coyly, the females saunter by the groups of performing males, seemingly distracted by other considerations, or at least unimpressed by all the commotion. The closest males become frantic, waving, as if to say, "Hey babe, look at the size of my manly claw." (In the case of fiddlers, the size of the male organ really is paramount.) "Would you like to come down and see my etchings?" Having surreptitiously considered her many suitors, the female chooses the male with the largest claw. Suddenly, and without fanfare, she darts down into his burrow, with the resident male right behind.

A male will also use the size of his claw to claim territory. In a border dispute, the male with the largest claw always wins without a fight. What happens, however, when the two opposing males have claws of equal size? It is in this instance, that two of our fiddler crab species earn their Latin names: Uca pugnax and Uca pugilator. The two males will grapple, box, and fence until the more doughty of the two pummels his opponent into submission. They are indeed a pugnacious lot.

Third Week of September
Martian Tides

So rarely seen, we would never imagine how many marsh hens live within the tidal margins of the Southeast Coast, were it not for their distinctive clapping call. Most of us do not know many bird calls, but if you live near the salt marshes, this is one with which you are probably familiar. The series of loud, nonmusical clacks, which tends to accelerate toward the end, sounds almost like a dry, cackling laugh. The commonly heard call is an intrinsic element of life in the tidelands.

When one male starts, he is usually answered by others even before he is finished. To me, they often sound like mischievous marsh spirits laughing at our frail human condition. When I lived near the salt marsh, I would be working outside in the yard. No sooner would I drop something on my foot, or hit my head, and the puckish laughter would emanate from the marsh—the rude spirits concealing themselves naughtily in the thick cordgrass: "Lord, what fools these mortals be!"

Many folks, even of those who know their call, have never seen a marsh hen. What do they look like? Try to look up "marsh hen" in your field guide to birds and you will remain clueless. "Marsh hen" may be what maritime folks call them, but ornithologists refer to them as "clapper rails." The "clapper" part obviously refers to their unique call. The "rail" part is a bit harder to figure. "Raile" is a Middle English word for the family of wetlands birds to which the marsh hen belongs. You have certainly heard the word before in a common expression referring to their appearance, although you probably misunderstood it.

The marsh hen is a typical rail: a crouching, chickenlike bird with a longer beak for probing into fiddler crab holes and marsh mud. When moving with purpose, they walk like Groucho Marx,

taking big steps with their head thrust far forward. They are almost half the size of a barnyard hen, but much, much thinner. What's more, rails are renowned by birdwatchers and hunters for being capable of compressing themselves to be even thinner, into a nearly two-dimensional bird, when escaping through the thick marsh grass stalks. The origin of the expression "thin as a rail" refers to these birds; not, as usually assumed, to locomotive rails. That this idea may be surprising is evidence that the figure of speech arose in a nontechnological age when people were far closer to the earth than they are today. The expression far predates the railroad age, but has come to refer to it in the minds of most Americans.

In the present season, clapper rails are still in mated pairs, patrolling their patch of salt marsh for snails, small crabs, and other marine invertebrates. They are one of only a handful of bird species who can tolerate the harsh, salty environment well enough to actually nest within the tidal marshes. To compensate for the constantly fluctuating water level, they usually choose their nest sites toward the edge of the marsh where only the highest tides reach. Then they build their low, flat nests out of the rack of dead materials washed up by the tides, mostly last year's dead cordgrass stalks. These materials float. So when an especially high tide comes in, the marsh hen nest floats up with it, eggs and all.

The best times to catch a glimpse of a marsh hen are during these high tides of the full and new moon phases. Although clapper rails can swim, they tend to follow the rising edge of the spring tidewater, catching the fiddler crabs who do the same, until they are right up on the edge of dry land and human habitations. Keen observers of nature can actually observe the producers of all that clapping in the marsh during these tides, occasionally referred to as "marsh hen tides."

Once a visitor to the tidelands, overhearing my talk about "marsh hen tides," approached me and remarked that she never knew the planet Mars also affected our tides. She had heard only the tail end of my story. I was puzzled by her question, so I tried to clear up the matter. Her expression turned incredulous when she heard me say that there are far more Martians in the salt marshes than most people realize.

Fourth Week of September
The Butterflies of Fall

Butterflies seem to be more noticeable this time of year than any other. They flutter about our lawns, gardens, and roadsides, seeking out the bright blossoms of fall asters and sunflowers. Three types are most abundant now in the Southeast: cloudless yellow sulphurs, gulf fritillaries (orange with silver streaks), and one species in particular, the long-tailed skipper.

Members of the skipper family earn their name by their rapid, darting flight. Known for their muted brownish colors, they all look very similar. The long-tailed skipper, however, is distinctively adorned with swept-back projections on its hind wings, not unlike those on the larger, more colorful swallowtail butterflies. Long-tailed skippers regularly find their way into screened-in porches and other man-made structures, where they often perish. When these lifeless unfortunates are examined more closely, their seemingly drab bodies and wings gleam faintly iridescent with a beautiful autumn array of forest greens, rusty ochres, and chocolate browns.

Skippers are not moths, but they are not quite butterflies either. They possess characteristics of both of these groups. Moths have furry bodies, drabber coloration, and feathery antennae. They have a tendency toward nocturnal habits. (Actually, there are very many exceptions to this popular idea of what defines a moth.) Also, as caterpillars, moths spin silken cocoons.

Butterflies, on the other hand, tend to have smoother bodies, brighter colors, and threadlike antennae with knobbed ends and are active during the day (diurnal). Unknown to many of us, however, is the fact that, unlike moths, butterfly caterpillars never make cocoons. Butterfly caterpillars make what biologists call a chrysalis, a hardened shell made from their own inner skin. The chrysalis hangs bare to the elements, with nothing resembling a cocoon around it.

Skippers seem to be a cross between the two. Skippers have furry bodies and muted colors like a moth. Diurnal like a butterfly, they also have the knobbed, threadlike antennae, but always with a distinctive hook on the end. However, when skipper caterpillars are ready to undergo the long pupation and metamorphosis into winged adults, they spin silk similar to moth caterpillars. The resulting creation, though, resembles no typical cocoon.

Gardeners and other keen observers of nature's minute details may often have found plants that have among their many normal leaves a leaf that is curiously doubled over on itself. Looking like the capricious contrivance of a faery seamstress, the leaf halves are not joined by stitches, but cemented together from the inside by adhesive silken threads. When the leaf halves are pulled apart, the curious naturalist finds a ruined ring of silk, formerly book-ended by two walls of green leaf. This pupal hideaway is a family trademark, the unique metamorphosis envelope of the skippers.

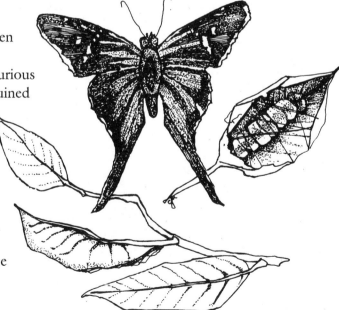

October

First Week of October
King of Snakes

W hat is purple, ten feet long, and eats rattlesnakes for breakfast? The "king of snakes" is the largest and longest-lived snake in North America, with an average life span of over a quarter of a century. Named the indigo snake for its dark, glossy skin, its smooth violet scales make it perhaps our most beautiful as well. To be in the presence of an indigo snake is to sense his royalty, fittingly clad in regal purple, with large, black eyes that seem to possess all knowledge of the many subjects of his wild realm. If lions are king of the jungle, indigo snakes are certainly king of the pine forests in the Southeast.

Once common in the coastal plain of the Southeast, indigo snakes are now a threatened species in this area and protected under the federal Endangered Species Act. Nearly all of our wild pine forests have been converted into quick-rotation tree farms for paper production. Such farms do not provide much habitat for wildlife. Being a top predator, the indigo snake needs large areas of undisturbed habitat in which to find sufficient prey. Since in the natural world, all things are connected, it comes as no surprise that the fate of the indigo is linked to another endangered species, the gopher tortoise.

This tortoise digs deep burrows that provide one of the few refuges for ground-dwelling creatures from summer heat, drought, and periodic fire in the pine forest. These holes, wherein the temperature and humidity change little, are a haven for many species: insects, toads, frogs, mice, and snakes, some of which are found nowhere else. All of these species get along fine with the tortoise, but not necessarily with each other. Since the king of snakes eats almost any smaller creature, he rarely shares his burrow with other guests, at least not for long. This time of year, indigos are actively hunting to store fat for the coming winter, when they will be forced to fast and hole up in tortoise burrows during the colder weather.

Indigo snakes eat primarily rodents, birds, lizards, and other snakes. One of their specialties is killing and eating venomous snakes, even full-grown cottonmouths and diamondbacks! To see an indigo eat a rattlesnake is as thrilling a hunt as there exists in the natural world. Unlike most large snakes, the indigo does not constrict its prey, but uses its powerful jaws to crush and kill. The indigo tracks the rattler's scent with his sensitive forked tongue. The rattler, which eats primarily warm-blooded animals, like mice, has a heat-sensitive pit below its eye. As the rattler is searching for evidence of body heat, the indigo, who is as cold-blooded as the rattler, creeps up undetected until it is too late. The indigo, fast as purple lightning, gasps the rattler behind its head so it cannot strike back, and begins to crush the rattler's skull. The two large reptiles thrash and entwine one another, but in a few moments the struggle is over, and the king of snakes is victorious. He then begins to swallow the elongate body of his victim, whole, of course, as always.

Ironically, a second reason why indigos are disappearing has to do with rattlesnakes. Landowners and rattlesnake roundup volunteers know that rattlers live in tortoise burrows. A common practice is to pour gasoline through a long hose into the burrow. The deadly fumes force the rattler from the excavation to be killed or caught. The fumes often do permanent damage to the lungs of any creature in the hole, indigos and rattlers alike. And most regrettably, the rare tortoise, too slow to make the quick exit required, dies immediately, and another crucial burrow-maker is removed from the ecosystem.

Thirdly, this beautiful snake is endangered precisely because it is so beautiful. Its appearance and its docile (with humans) nature make it a favorite among snake collectors and pet owners. It has

literally been collected to the point of extirpation in some areas. I'll never forget visiting a collector once, about a decade ago, before the species was protected by law. I held his indigo snake in my own two hands. It was over nine feet long and as big around as a tennis ball. Its scales glistened with the truest of dark purples. It was the friendliest, most magnificent snake I've ever held, and although I'm largely opposed to keeping wild animals in captivity, I admit I experienced the desire in myself to possess this awesome creature, and understood why it is the favorite among snake collectors.

Since that time, I have learned more about the plight of the indigo as a species. I have also gained an understanding about natural beauty. It is true that few of us will ever experience the beauty of an indigo snake in the wild. But just knowing they are out there enriches our appreciation of the diverse and intricate world we live in, assuring us that nature is in balance and the web of life is as it should be.

Second Week of October
Flower Kisser

The year is 1500. Pedro Alvares Cabral steps into the thick jungle of what will soon become the Portuguese colony of Brazil. Amid the verdant growth of the rain forest understory are bright red tubular flowers that stand out in striking contrast to the deep ubiquitous greenness. Admiring them, he is startled to notice the largest bee he has ever seen at the mouth of one of the flowers. It darts suddenly from the flower and hovers right in front of his face as if studying the red velvet of his collar. Upon closer examination. Cabral begins to realize that this is no bee. It has a long, narrow beak, is covered with scintillating feathers of bright green and blue, and is glaring at him with two dark, birdlike eyes.

Unbelievably, it begins to dawn on him that this tiny creature is a bird, but it is so small! And it is suspended in midair like no bird he has ever seen. The explorer has observed nothing like it in all his travels through Europe and Africa. He watches it, mesmerized, as it grows bored with him and turns its attention back to the flowers, visiting each briefly, but never landing, hovering to lick nectar with its very long tongue. He had no name to call this fascinating creature, but the Portuguese colonists after him were to name it "beija-flor," or flower kisser.

Farther north, English colonists named these birds after another of their peculiar behaviors. In order to hover insectlike, their wings beat so fast that they actually hum. And so they named them hummingbirds. The English were no less amazed by them than other Europeans, because hummingbirds are only found in the New World. Of the many new sights and discoveries awaiting the white man in the Americas, the very existence of hummingbirds was not the least.

And when we see them visiting the trumpet creepers in our own backyard, are we much less enthralled, despite the fact that we are well aware of their existence? It is always a thrill to watch them hovering and darting quickly from place to place. Their wings, unlike those of other birds, rotate so as to achieve lift and power on both the fore and back strokes, allowing them to hover in place, as well as locomote with great efficiency. These tiny birds have been clocked at speeds of over thirty miles per hour. Much to the frustration of people who would like to admire their radiant plumage, they rarely stay still long enough. Lowering her binoculars in exasperation one day, my wife assigned a new name to them: "jet jewels." And who would not be hyperactive with such a sugary diet? Their ultrahigh metabolic rate is so intense that they must assume a hibernation-like state each night in order to avoid starving to death in their sleep.

Their specialized tongues, longer than their beaks, are tubular at the ends and tipped with brushy fibers for nectar extraction. To add the necessary protein to their sweet diet, they eat small insects, an abundance of which can be found around flowers. It is not unusual to see our hummingbirds inspecting the eaves of neighboring houses, searching for spiderwebs. Their unique hovering ability allows them to pluck spiders and entangled insects from the webs. Female hummingbirds will also steal away with strands of the webbing as well.

The female builds her own nest of soft materials like fern leaves and thistle down, binding it all together with spider and caterpillar silk, then camouflaging the outside with lichens and moss. A favorite nesting spot is a thin, horizontal branch, sheltered overhead by leaves, overhanging a stream. The whole structure is about the size of half a walnut shell. The two white eggs inside are so minuscule that they resemble improbably placed Tic Tac mints, lying side by side.

Male hummers are shamelessly polygamous. Courtship is brief. The female raises the young on her own. She also defends her own territory from other females and males alike. She is a feisty supermom. She will battle with bumblebees for possession of her favorite flowers. She will harass other birds, even eagles, who fly through her air space.

Here in the Southeast, we have but one nesting species, the ruby-throated hummingbird. The farther south you go, the more different species you may encounter. A single South American habitat type may include over a dozen species: hummers with crests, long tails, beaks like small scimitars, brilliant colors—the variety seems endless. The hummer diversity in the tropics has led biologists to theorize that hummingbird evolution probably began in equatorial Latin America. Sometime after the two continents began to converge, hummers spread gradually north, along with the wildflower species that have evolved the red tubular flowers designed to attract hummingbirds as pollinators. Most North American species still winter in the tropics. About this time of year, our ruby-throated hummers will soon be crossing the Gulf of Mexico in an astounding nonstop flight—relative to their diminutive size, surely one of the natural world's most impressive migrations. This winter, they will be visiting with their ancient relatives, kissing flowers with the best of them.

Third Week of October
Little Armored One

Rustle, rustle … CRASH. You are suddenly awake inside your tent. Your heart is trying to pound its way out of your chest, the way it does only when you are awakened by a loud noise. You are very alert now, listening, your ears straining. Silence …, then THUMP. Your eyes widen in the darkness. More rustling. Your tentmate is sleeping through all this. Then footsteps, HEAVY footsteps, through the underbrush, coming toward the tent. "Oh God, it's a bear," you think to yourself. You don't move or make a sound. You consider waking your partner. "No, better to be sure, don't want to look like a wimp." You rationalize: "Maybe it's just a lost horse or something. There aren't really any bears around here …, are there? Better take a look outside." Ever so quietly, you press your nose against the mosquito netting and peer through it timidly, toward the source of the sounds. Your eyes are adjusted to the dark. You don't dare use your flashlight. Maybe the bear would charge if startled.

The moonlight casts interlacing tree limb shadows on the forest floor. Amidst the dappled pattern of light spots, you spy a rounded shape, not ten feet away. But it's not large at all. Not even as big as a 'coon. The moonlight glistens off the creature's back like something shiny. "How could anything so small make so much racket?" You can hear it digging and snuffling. It moves again. It doesn't pick up its feet to walk. Why, it doesn't even pick up its face to walk. It is pushing through the leaf litter as it moves, like a little bulldozer. Its nose is buried in the dirt, sniffing intently.

Enough of this. You open the tent flap, now full of indignant bravado. The sound of the zipper tears through the forest silence. The startled armadillo leaps straight upward, then bounds like a rabbit straight into the briar patch. Crash, crash, then a sound like a running child's stick along a picket fence, as the stiff palmetto stems rasp along the ridges of the fleeing creature's armored back. Finally now, your tentmate wakes up. "What's goin' on?" he asks. You reply, "There was something outside the tent, but I scared it off." Then slyly you add, "Probably just a bear."

The Spanish conquistadors had seen nothing like it in the Old World. Their explorations through Central and South America introduced them to many marvels, both cultural and natural. Not the least among them was the discovery of a wild animal that appeared to be covered with armor. Perhaps they saw in this small creature an image of themselves, vested in breastplates and helmeted, crashing their way through the strange tropical underbrush. They named it, endearingly, the "little armored one," in Spanish, armadillo (they pronounced it "armadeeyo").

But when the conquistadors explored what would later become Texas, Florida, and Georgia, they found no armadillos. There were none here. Armadillos are a recent addition to the wildlife of the Southeast. Apparently, before 1800, there were none in the United States. They were always known to be abundant in Mexico. John J. Audubon described the first armadillo in this country in the 1850s, in south Texas. From there, having crossed the barrier of the Rio Grande, they spread rapidly northward. By the 1930s, armadillos had found their way into Oklahoma, Arkansas, and Louisiana. Then, suddenly, a disjunct population sprouted up on the east coast of Florida about this same time.

The story of how armadillos came to Florida is not well known, but it is clear that people had a hand in it. In 1922, a young boy caught one near the city of Miami. He took the mysterious creature to the Miami Zoo. The staff there could hardly believe that wild armadillos lived in Florida. But further investigation confirmed that indeed they did. A marine from Texas, who had been stationed at Hialeah during the First World War, admitted to releasing a pair after one of his furloughs home. Another pair had escaped from a small zoo in Cocoa. Apparently, a few chance occurrences such as these were all it took.

It seems that armadillos are ideally suited to the ecology of the Southeast. It would, perhaps, come as no surprise that these armored creatures have trouble crossing big rivers. Once they do, however, they are off and run-ning. For a while they seemed stuck on the south side of the St. Mary's River. Then in 1970, they started showing up in Georgia. By 1975, they had arrived at the south bank of the Savannah River. Since  then, the ranges of the eastward-moving Texas clan and the west-ward-moving Florida clan have merged along the Florida panhandle. Now, armadillos have made their way well into South Carolina. There is a limit to how far north they will eventually go, however. Armadillos, being tropical creatures, have not evolved the ability to hibernate. Even if they had enough insulation to keep from freezing in winter, they would likely starve farther north than the Carolinas, due to their reliance on insects and other cold-blooded creatures as dietary staples.

Although they have sometimes been considered agricultural pests, accused of causing crop damage, these charges have been mis-placed. In search of grubs and worms in the soil, armadillos will dig. They also dig deep burrows to live in. So it's possible that they can damage gardens, but only incidentally. Although the destruction could conceivably be great to the small plot of an unlucky gardener, agriculturally speaking, armadillos could never cause significant losses on a grand scale.

No wimpy vegetarians, these guys. And armadillos will eat more than just grubs. They will tear into a fire ant mound with gusto, undaunted by the wicked stings inflicted on their soft underbellies and sensitive noses. A typical Mexican immigrant, they like their food HOT. One road-killed individual was found in Texas with the following stomach contents: ten tarantulas, one scorpion, a small snake, and a toad! Here is a critter worthy of the Lone Star State. The armadillo has been officially recognized as the state mammal of Texas.

Yes, they are mammals, though they look almost reptilian. The armored "shell," unique in the order Mammalia, is actually a modified skin layer that has evolved a bonelike hardness. Not surprisingly, the armadillo family is most closely related to the anteaters of South America. In the New World tropics there are many different species of armadillos. The most northerly species, and the one we now have in the Southeast, is the "nine-banded armadillo," so named for the number of wide ridges across the middle of its back.

Now is the mating season of the nine-banded armadillo in the Southeast. They breed in fall, but do not give birth until late spring, even though their gestation period is less than five months long. Armadillos can delay implantation of the fertilized egg for months, until the time is right. Actually, delayed implantation is not uncommon in the animal world. But one other aspect of armadillo reproduction is absolutely unique. When implantation in the uterus finally does occur, the fertilized egg always splits into four identical quarters, before further development ensues. Without exception, armadillos give birth only to identical quadruplets.

This obscure fact has proven important to the medical research community. Much to the dismay of animal rights activists, there are many areas of research where the use of genetically identical individuals can be very helpful when subjecting separate individuals to different treatments. Another obscure armadillo fact is that armadillos are the only nonprimate species on the planet affected by leprosy. To produce the vaccine that prevents this poorly understood disease, labs must have a ready source of the living pathogen. Captive infected armadillos can serve as a reliable resource from which to obtain this bacteria.

Leprosy is the least contagious of infectious human diseases. How it is contracted is poorly understood. The percentage of wild armadillos that carry leprosy is very small, especially in the Southeast. It is thought that nine-banded armadillos contracted leprosy originally from humans, somewhere in Mexico or Texas.

Despite this, people eat armadillos. Long valued as a source of meat in Mexico, armadillo became an important food in Texas during the Depression, when they were tauntingly referred to as "Hoover hogs." These days country folks still eat armadillo. Since some folks, even those accustomed to all manners of wild game, might object to the idea of eating armadillo, it is sometimes referred to lightheartedly as "possum on the half shell."

Fourth Week of October
Early Air Mail

*F*our days before news of Napoleon's defeat at Waterloo arrived by courier on horseback, the lords of London knew of the Duke of Wellington's great victory. Similarly, Rome was kept abreast of Caesar's military exploits in the distant land of the Gauls by an early form of airmail. At some point, after thousands of years of domestication as simply a source of meat, humans discovered a fascinating behavior in the pigeons they were raising.

Imagine how this discovery might have taken place. A young bride leaves her family to marry a man in another village. As part of her dowry, some pigeons are sent in a cage made of cane. During the journey through the hill country, the cage falls from the back of the donkey and bursts asunder. The pigeons fly out. The family watches helplessly as the pigeons circle higher and higher into the sky. In their consternation, no one in the party notices the significance of the direction the pigeons have chosen when they fly off. But days later, when the parents return to their village after the wedding, they find, to their amazement, all the lost pigeons roosting atop the coop behind the home, waiting to be fed.

Pigeons were probably the first domesticated bird species, beginning as early as 4500 B.C. Such incidents as the above probably happened many times before some bright individual conceived of an application for this marvelous behavior. Taking the pigeon farther and farther from its coop with each release, the first trainers realized a primitive, but effective express mail delivery system. As with many inventions, development of the system probably received its greatest impetus when someone applied it to military operations. Sufficiently speedy communication was always one of an army's greatest limiting factors during a large-scale campaign. Even as late as the First World War, homing pigeons were used for sending secret communiqués.

We have all heard of the bird called a carrier pigeon, but few of us realize that we see this species every day. Most imagine them to be a specialized member of the dove family seen only by homing pigeon enthusiasts. Look out your window. There they are on the sidewalk, flying overhead, or perched atop General Jackson's bronze epaulets. The pigeon we see strutting about in every city and village around the globe is a carrier pigeon in the rough.

Native to Eurasia, the forebears of our common city pigeons nested in rocky places from the Himalayas to the cliffs of Dover. The French first introduced them to this continent in the 1600s. Through their usefulness as message carriers, they have been transported all over the world. Lost homing pigeons and escapees have naturally been drawn to the dwellings of people. Especially in flat country, like the rockless environment of the Southeast Coast, where no cliffs are found, a pigeon would instinctively use the window ledge of an office building as a surrogate nest site. In England, and in your bird book, these birds are named "rock doves," due to their original propensity for mountainside roosts.

A symbiotic relationship has developed between humans and rock doves over the centuries. Only a few cultures still regularly include pigeon meat in their cuisine. (If you find this concept objectionable, you may want to pass up the bistilla on the next visit to your favorite Moroccan restaurant.) And express mail by carrier pigeon has been relegated to the rare hobbyist by superior postal service and modern telecommunications. But pigeons benefit greatly from the doings of humans. There would be no place for them to thrive on the Southeast Coast, were it not for us. Also, watch them this time of year in the streets and sidewalks beneath the sprawling live oaks of Savannah and Charleston. Rock doves love the acorns that oaks drop in the fall. But they use us as their nutcracker servants. Our hard-soled shoes and heavy motorized treads spare them the trauma of attempting to crack a rolling, thick-shelled food source with their own tender beaks.

November

First Week of November
The Premier Fisherman

"**A**re there any fish in this lake?" You have to wonder to yourself. You've been fishing for hours without a nibble. Suddenly, a large bird comes out of nowhere and flies over the lake. It hovers briefly, thirty feet over a spot where you had just been fishing. The hawklike creature looks down for a moment, then drops feet-first into the water. Splash. Wet wings flap. The bird rises up from the water, a large fish wriggling in its talons. It flies toward your boat. A momentary spasm seizes the bird in midair as it shakes the water from its feathers. Directly over your head now, it looks at you askance. "Cheert-cheert-cheert," it calls. It seems to be saying, "Silly human, you can't catch fish if you're not willing to get wet."

The osprey, or fish hawk, is a familiar site in the Southeast. Over any of our lakes, rivers, marsh creeks, or even over the ocean along our beaches, you can see ospreys flying about and fishing. Their success rate is amazing to watch. Ball players would love to have such a batting average. They rarely miss. They are the envy of any of us who love to fish.

Osprey fishing success is due to some special adaptations. One of the ways to distinguish ospreys from other hawks at a glance is to note the distinctive bend at the osprey's wrists. Hawks and eagles tend to hold their wings straight out, like a plank. The unique bend in the wing helps the osprey hover in place, while it looks directly down at its prey. This technique avoids what herons and spear fishermen must contend with, the distortion that comes from viewing them at an angle, due to light refraction through the water. The wing shape also allows ospreys to take off, straight out of the water, something other hawks would not be able to do.

Like most fishing birds, the osprey's eyes contain a special pigment, called visual purple, that cuts through the glare on the water's surface, allowing him to see fish clearly. The osprey's talons are also different from those of other hawks. They have two toes pointing forward and two backward, so they can get a better grip on their slippery prey. In addition, toward this end, they have spines in the pads of their toes. To see an osprey flying with a fish in its talons is not only a common site, it is a lesson in aerodynamics. The next time you see one with a fish, note how the osprey always turns the fish's head in the direction of travel, one talon in front of the other, to make the fish more streamlined during flight.

Of all our fishing birds, the only other one to catch with talons instead of a beak is the bald eagle. Eagles, however, are too large to hover in place or to take off out of the water. Their broad, straight wings, with a span of eight feet, make them strong fliers who can soar almost endlessly.

But when it comes time to hunt, they must snag their fish off the surface as they fly over the water. Consequently, the bald eagle's fishing success rate is not nearly as great as the osprey's. This fact sets up an adversarial relationship between the two species, with our national bird playing the considerably larger, but less talented, bully. The eagle, being the more powerful flier, will chase down an osprey whose claws are grasping a fish. I have witnessed this confrontation many times, especially in the Everglades, and it is always a sight to behold. The two raptors swoop and dive like fighter planes in a dogfight, the eagle right on the tail of the osprey, until the osprey finally releases the fish. At this point the eagle immediately whirls and dives to make a spectacular catch of the fish before it hits the ground. To watch such a large bird achieve a high-speed midair grab on such short notice is astounding. But now the tables are turned. The eagle's talons are occupied and the osprey's are free. The eagle has no time to waste. The faster eagle, however, is able to outpace the pursuing osprey, though the chase may continue far into the distance.

Second Week of November
Life in the Surf Zone

*T*he sandpipers match their pace to the rhythm of the surf. They scurry at the edge of the foam with each passing wave. They seem always about to be engulfed, but they never are. These birds race along the ever-moving line, charging, retreating, and probing into the sand with quick thrusts of their beaks. They are so intent on their role. This time of year, the sandpipers are very common, hunting the beaches of the Southeast Coast. Why are they probing the sand in such a precarious place? The sand seems barren of life. What prey could be living in there?

On closer examination, you notice many small holes in the sand. Some of these bubble as the waves slide back over them. Animals, it seems, are living down there, but why? Who are they, and how do they make a living in such an inhospitable habitat?

The sand beneath the beach is alive with small creatures: mole crabs, polychaete worms, coquina clams, and many others. Existing in the surf zone, they are protected by the pounding waves and the variable water level from many of the predators that hunt either the ocean or the land. Only a few hunters can dodge the waves like the sandpipers do. Most of the small surf zone animals feed by filtering plankton from the sea water, a common way of life among marine creatures in general. But by living here, they are safe from the marauding of large fish and predatory crabs of the ocean.

Surf zone creatures burrow under the sand. Most are quite tiny and have no permanent burrow. To find the home of one of the largest and most advanced of these specialized animals, however, look for a hole almost a quarter of an inch in diameter. Scattered around the hole will be a cluster of minute, chocolate-colored cylinders that resemble nothing so much as the sugary "jimmies" that are sprinkled over the tops of ice cream cones. These, of course, are the telltale feces of the creature within. Here lives a specialized kind of shrimp that, rather than swimming and schooling in our coastal waters, spends its entire adult life in a subterranean chamber of its own making. This creature lives in darkness, its pinpoint eyes staring upward to the one source of dim light in its world, the sole opening of the burrow. The burrow widens immediately below the hole to house this elongated shrimp that can be four inches long. Protected by its dark burrow, its shell is as thin as parchment and spectral white, giving this creature its common name: "ghost shrimp."

We rarely see this delicate species because it is so secretive. At best we see signs of their filter feeding activity as they force water out of their holes by beating appendages on their abdomen. Like most shrimp, they are perfectly edible and delicious. The problem is catching them. Their long cylindrical chamber can be six feet in length, and ghost shrimp move quickly downward at the first sign of digging or probing from above.

Since digging them out is nigh impossible, or at least impractical, some hungry seafood lovers have developed more devious means of capturing ghost shrimp. Ghost shrimp are fastidious about keeping their burrows clean. If you sprinkle sand down the entrance, the ghost shrimp will eventually rise to push the sand out with its long, white claw. But when it happens, it happens fast. So you must patiently sprinkle with one hand while keeping the other poised for the grab. There certainly are easier ways of procuring a fresh seafood dinner.

Third Week of November
Hit and Miss

*F*inally escaping from Jurassic Park, the exhausted paleontologist gazes out the window of the rescue helicopter that is whisking him to safety, and notices a flock of pelicans gliding over the Pacific. A faint smile forms on his lips. Their resemblance to pterosaurs is uncanny. It is as if he is thinking: "This is how it should remain, dinosaurs are extinct forever, but their natural descendants, the birds, live on."

How fitting an end to a movie about the genetically engineered creation of present-day dinosaurs. Many times from the beach I have gazed over the ocean to watch the brown pelicans soaring above. They always reminded me of pterodactyls with their long, broad wings and their bizarre head shape. The resemblance is not the result of ancestry actually, but of convergent evolution. Pterosaurs have no living descendants. They were a reptilian branch separate from the dinosaurs that gave rise to modern-day birds. But long wings and large bills are as ideal for gliding on ocean breezes and catching fish today as in Jurassic times.

Watching brown pelicans catch fish is a mesmerizing pastime for a lazy day at the beach. Diving from great heights and twisting to keep one eye on the target, these large birds crash into the water headfirst. They employ their famous pouches as fishnets, in which to capture small fish underwater.

The typical stylized cartoon pelican is drawn standing up with his pouch distended by a large fish whose tail might be protruding from his beak. Actually it is rare to see a pelican with his pouch full, unless perhaps you are a scuba diver. Many beach-goers actually have trouble identifying these common birds as pelicans, because the pouch is not visible, being drawn tight under the long beak in flight. Their pouch is distended only under water, and then only for the few seconds it takes them to drain the water off their fish catch. And this catch is rarely a large fish. Generally, the brown pelican is searching for schools of small fish, like anchovies, that he can dive into, hopefully capturing a few of the many individuals in his "net"—a technique that works poorly for larger or solitary fish.

Once, while snorkeling in the clear waters of the Galapagos Islands, I managed to observe and photograph the procedure underwater. After monitoring an individual's fishing behavior for a few minutes, I managed to be close enough when the pelican dove into the water. The bird's upper mandible thrust into the water like a spear, while the lower half of the beak spread open the pouch into a

barely visible school of tiny fish. The whole action is so instantaneous, that I didn't really expect to see what happens, but instead
snapped a photo with my underwater camera, at what I hoped was
the right instant. When returning home, I eagerly developed the roll
to see what, if anything, I had captured on film. And there it was,
amidst a froth of bubbles, the pelican's pouch was distended underwater like a dull gray balloon.

It is fun to sit on any beach of the Southeast and watch the
pelican's rate of success. Compared to other fishing birds, like the
osprey whose talons rarely miss, brown pelicans have an inferior
record. Once you've observed them for a while, it is easy to determine when a pelican has caught anything. Watch the pelican's head
immediately after the dive. The head of a pelican who has missed
pops back up to the normal head-held-high position quickly as if to
appear nonchalant: "Who me? I wasn't tryin' to catch anything
really. Just swimmin' along here's all." But a pelican who has scored
holds his head down close to the water for a bit in order to drain the
pouch slowly through its barely open beak while retaining the
anchovies. When he brings his head up, he immediately tilts his head
back to swallow his prize. During this swallowing maneuver is the
best time to see the pelican's pouch.

In order to judge a pelican fairly, however, you need to look at
its plumage. This time of year, the pelicans with the best records
tend to have bright white necks and yellow foreheads (or rich
chocolate-brown necks and white heads in summer breeding
plumage). These are the adults. They have got the technique down.
Now watch the young pelicans that are all a scruffy gray-brown.
Their miss rate can be vicariously frustrating. There's nothing like
experience to make an expert fisherman.

Fourth Week of November
Ant's Nightmare

*I*n bare spots protected from rain, under the eaves of a house or shed, one may notice curious conical depressions in soft sandy soil. These small pits have little consequence in the lives of the Southeast's human residents, but to ants and other small crawling insects they represent a grisly doom. They are the deadly traps constructed by a ferocious little insect appropriately called the ant lion.

In the Southeast, they are often called "doodlebugs" because of the scrawling, looping tracks they leave as they back-pedal through the surface of the sand when out of their traps. Actually, the ant lion is the larval stage of a small dragonfly-like insect called, not surprisingly, "the ant lion fly," making it one of the few insect species named after the characteristics of the larva, rather than of the adult.

As larvae, ant lions have flat heads with jaws like huge pinchers. They create their traps by using their heads like a shovel, tossing sand up and out of the pit. The result is a sunken cone of loose sand with a slope that seems perfectly engineered for causing a "sandslide" when disturbed. Ants find themselves slipping toward the center of the pit, where wait the gaping jaws of the hungry ant lion.

The trap does not always work. Some of the prey escape. If the ant lion senses his prey is gaining on the lip of the trap, he will use his flat head to flick sand at the ant, hastening the sandslide effect. The ant lion can be stimulated to demonstrate this behavior by lightly tickling the sides of the pit with a pine needle tip to mimic an ant in the trap. Children of the Southeast have developed this into a sort of ritual, chanting a "doodlebug" rhyme reserved espccially for this occasion. When accomplished with the sort of expertise that

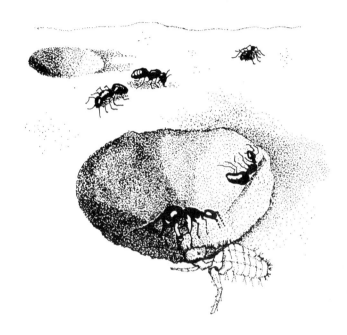

only children can bring to bear on such activities, the ant lion, normally buried under the sand, will then start slinging sand and expose his lethal mandibles.

The ant lion has inspired many Hollywood monsters in science fiction movies, such as Enemy Mine and Return of the Jedi. It seems we cannot help but imagine what life would be like in a landscape where human-sized versions lurked in such treacherous lairs.

December

First Week of December
V Is for Vulture

The two cartoon buzzards are perched, stoop-shouldered, on a tall snag, overlooking a barren desert landscape. The hot sun is beating down on their featherless heads. Time wears on. Suddenly, the left one blurts out, "To heck with this waiting around all the time, I'm gonna go KILL somethin'!"

Patience must, indeed, be a common virtue among vulture-kind. When you let other forces do your killing for you, you learn how to wait, even when hungry. We see them soaring endlessly, high in the sky above us, rarely even flapping. With their long, black wings held up at an angle, forming a subtle "V" in the sky, they tilt side to side with the wind currents. At such a distance they appear as dark overlords of the air, and possess a certain beauty of form and majesty. "Vulture" seems a fitting name for one so lofty and masterful.

Face to face, of course, is another story. Our other name for them, "buzzard," seems more appropriate up close. Their naked heads appear ugly to us. Their beady eyes stare at us, and we are reminded of their function in the natural world. It makes us uneasy. We know this scavenger wishes death for us, death for all the earthbound who crawl across the ground below. We reassure ourselves of our immediate health and well-being. But they force us to consider our mortality. Vultures are the black-vested undertakers of the wild realm. They serve an important role. But their method of handling the body appalls us. Yet this is Nature's way, of course. Nothing is wasted.

With meal availability beyond their control, vultures have evolved an economy of motion that allows them to function on a low-energy budget. Opportunities to eat may be spaced many days apart. In a sense, they are solar-powered birds, who let the wind do the work of flying for them. During the cool night, the body temperature of a vulture drops. Unlike most warm-blooded animals, their temperature varies regularly because their metabolism is so slow. Come morning, they spread their wings and turn their backs to the rising sun. Their black feathers quickly absorb the solar warmth. Their alertness sharpens. As the sun climbs, it strikes different surfaces at different angles. The hillside facing the sun heats up faster than the plain. The water reflects more heat than the marsh. The forest remains cooler than the blacktop. Columns of hot air rise more forcefully from some surfaces than others, creating updrafts. Vultures ride expertly along the edges of these "thermals." By flying in tight circles, they can rise with the ascending air columns. Once they are aloft, their large wings, spanning six feet, carry them almost effortlessly onward in the long search for death.

The frontal "V" silhouette of a flying vulture is distinctive. Only turkey vultures employ this "dihedral" wing posture. Other soaring birds, like hawks and eagles, hold their wings straight out to either side, like a plank across their backs. Once you learn to look for the dihedral wings, you can impress your friends by recognizing a turkey vulture at great distances.

Our other species of buzzard, the black vulture, holds its wings flat out like a hawk, has a shorter wingspan, and, therefore, flaps a lot more; while the turkey vulture has a naked red face like his namesake, the black vulture's head is dark gray. The black vulture makes up for his lack of mastery of the air with agility on the ground. When food is found, vultures gather to the feast. Though turkey vultures may find the carrion first, due to their superior sense of smell and their ability to range more widely with less effort, they are built primarily for soaring and are more awkward on foot. The black vulture can outmaneuver the turkey vulture once at the carcass and, if the dead animal is small, even run the turkey vulture off.

Around garbage dumps, black vultures will scamper about like foraging chickens. They are a common element of Latin American market places, even in the middle of metropolitan areas. It is said that they used to frequent the central markets of downtown Charleston and Savannah. Because of their terrestrial scavenging habits, black vultures are more likely to encounter threats in tight places. For this situation, they have developed a defense behavior, especially effective against humans. Black vultures can regurgitate with awesome force. Who among us would brave an onslaught of vulture vomit? Whatever the ingredients, they were bound to be pretty disgusting the first time down, let alone brought up again.

To find carrion in the wild, buzzards not only watch for still, lifeless bodies below, they also watch each other. Especially, the black vultures watch the turkey vultures. Since a needle in a haystack can be more easily found by many searchers, vultures are very gregarious. Vultures roost together at night in remote areas. The number of individuals at a roost, especially at this time of year, can be quite large. Now, our turkey vulture numbers are bolstered by many northern birds down for the winter.

In response to the changes humans have wrought on the continent, buzzards have expanded their range in recent years. Naturally, such a scavenger would be very fond of the planet's most wasteful species. This century, a new dimension has clearly developed within the long symbiotic relationship between vultures and people, especially Americans sixteen or older. Road kills have become an important vulture food source. Nevertheless, the black vulture is a strictly southern species and nonmigratory. The turkey vulture, however, with its larger wing span, is able to soar even in southern Canada, where the summer sun is lower in the sky. But come winter, they must migrate south. Carrion hardens quickly in a northern winter, and even a buzzard beak cannot peck through frozen flesh.

The vulture instinct to roost together is so strong that they have developed a peculiar parenthood strategy. During the nesting season, vulture couples nest by themselves, apart from other buzzards. The two parents brood their hatchlings continuously for the first days of life. But as soon as the helpless young have sprouted downy feathers sufficient to keep themselves warm, the parents leave the chicks alone each night in order to join with other adults at the local roost! Here, perhaps, is a noteworthy system of parental priorities.

Second Week of December

Snake Bird

W hat a strange sight it is to see a bird swimming through the water with its body submerged and only its head above the surface. The head, no wider than the long neck to which it is attached, darts back and forth over the water, its long beak pointing to and fro. Just as quickly as it appeared, the head sinks below the surface again, to pop back up at some other surprisingly distant and unexpected spot moments later. Although a swimming snake would never raise its head so far above the water's surface, the sight of the bird's long neck and head sticking out of the water is indeed reminiscent of some kind of serpent, earning this unusual bird one of its many unusual names: snake bird.

Its official name is anhinga, an Indian word meaning "water turkey," also one of its English names. Its body, though much narrower than a wild turkey's, has much the same coloration and gives the same general impression, especially when the anhinga spreads its tail, which it often does underwater. Elsewhere in the world, it is called a darter because of the characteristic motions of its pointy head. Few birds have so many names, but this one has earned them all.

The anhinga is probably best known for its distinctive habit of perching with its wings spread wide. The story goes that the poor anhinga's ancestors never developed the oil glands of other water birds, and must, therefore, now dry its wings after swimming so that it can fly again. There is a popular misconception that evolution dealt the anhinga a bad hand. But nothing could be further from the truth.

While in the water hunting for fish, the anhinga does indeed become soaked to the skin, feathers and all. Water does not roll off an anhinga's back. However, this supposed shortcoming is actually to the anhinga's advantage, because of its unique hunting style. Water-repellent feathers would create an air pocket all over the surface of the bird's body, making the anhinga much more buoyant. The anhinga does not rest on the surface, diving at intervals like ducks, cormorants, and loons. The anhinga hunts underwater for extended periods of time. Were he to have waterproof feathers, the anhinga would have to constantly be fighting his own buoyancy to remain under the surface, like trying to stay underwater with a life jacket on.

Although it was once thought that bird oil glands were what made feathers water-repellent, biologists now know that it is the microscopic structure of the feathers themselves that sheds water. Anhingas have evolved especially permeable feathers to complement their own special style of fishing.

Although the task is much easier with dry feathers, anhingas can and do fly when wet. The main reason anhingas spread their wings has to do with the down side of possessing water-permeable feathers: poor insulation. When drenched, an anhinga, which has an unusually low metabolic rate anyway, loses body heat rapidly. When the air is cooler, but the sun is shining, anhingas will spread their wings and turn their backs to the sun, not just to dry out, but more important, to catch warmth from the sun. With their black feathers, the anhinga's spread wings act as efficient solar collectors.

Due to their lack of insulation, anhingas cannot tolerate colder climates, as other water birds do. Anhingas, and the rest of their cousins in the darter family, are found throughout the tropical and subtropical regions of the world. I have seen the same species we have in the Southeast throughout most of South America. But it does not occur much farther north than the coast of the Carolinas.

They avoid saltwater, so the best places to look for them are in lakes and swamps and along rivers throughout the coastal plain.

Unfortunately, in most such places in the Southeast, the water is too murky to watch the anhinga's artful fishing technique underwater. An anhinga doing his thing in clear water, in the Everglades or in one of Florida's spring runs, for instance, is an amazing sight to behold. Unlike other fish-eating birds who snatch up fish in their beaks, the anhinga actually spears its prey with his long, needle-sharp beak. When a fish, most often a sunfish or bluegill, is in range, the

anhinga "cocks" his neck, not unlike the way a heron does, but under water. Then he spreads his tail, turkey-fashion, as a brace for the strike. If successful, the anhinga surfaces with his skewered catch

wriggling on his beak, flicks his head back, tossing the fish upwards, then catches the fish in midair and swallows it whole, headfirst. Wow. One way, it is said, to tell the difference between an anhinga and its close relative, the cormorant, is that you will see a cormorant with a fish in its beak. But you will see an anhinga with its beak in a fish.

Third Week of December
How I Spent My Winter Vacation

The humidity seems almost visible amidst the huge columnar trunks of giant trees. The few sunbeams that pierce through the dense rain forest canopy appear as misty shafts of dull whiteness, dimly illuminating lush greenery. Oddly twisted vines and thin aerial roots, suspended in the shadows, hang from the thick, airplant-encrusted limbs of the spreading tree crowns above. The summer tanager flies up to a higher branch and looks out over the top of the rain forest. His plumage, the color of ripe raspberries, is now a dazzling red in the full sunlight.

Last summer, this bird nested in a neighborhood woodlot beside a house in Savannah, Georgia. But those charming live oaks and graceful antebellum houses are far behind him now. From his present vantage point, the top of the tropical forest canopy appears as an endless patchwork quilt laid over an irregular surface, with a thousand different shades of green. A troop of long-limbed spider monkeys is sampling fist-sized fruits in the top of a nearby tree. A pair of large green parrots wing overhead in frenetic flight, squawking noisily. In the distance, an anomalous structure crests above the treetops. "Perhaps it is a man-thing," he thinks, though it is apparently very old by the looks of the thick, tropical vegetation that covers all but a few gray walls of its ancient masonry. "There might be a bee colony there. They like that kind of place." He is hungry. Since the fruit-laden strangler fig tree he found while following the honeycreepers this morning, he has eaten just a few woodroaches.

"No use flying through the open air. The bat falcon will be hunting nearby, no doubt." The summer tanager hops back down below the rain forest canopy. Flitting from limb to limb, he makes his way toward the aged temple, ever watchful for the possibility of a well-camouflaged boa constrictor lying in ambush along the way. At the high crotch of a lightning-struck mahogany, a small flock of toucans are bathing in a suspended puddle, a penthouse birdbath. Their large, rainbow-colored beaks point this way and that as they preen and splash. He waits for them to finish, then indulges himself. Tiny tree frog tadpoles squiggle in the rotting bark at the bottom of the pool as he ruffles his feathers dry.

Upon arriving at his destination, he searches the nooks and crannies of the complex pyramid for the telltale entrance tube of a stingless bee colony. Finally, late in the afternoon, he finds the black, waxy funnel emerging from a large crack in a wall. Much like the ancient Mayans themselves had once done in search of honey, he now tears into the nest, but seeks instead the juicy grublike bodies of juvenile bees. The tiny black warriors fall upon his feathers biting furiously, but to little avail. When he has had enough, the summer tanager flies off to begin his search for a roost for the night. As the tropical sun quickly sets, the fearsome roar of howler monkeys echoes through the darkening rain forest.

Such are the secret lives of many southern songbirds. Though they spend their summers with us, they migrate far south to winter in tropical latitudes between Mexico and Brazil. Many, like our summer tanager, are wintering, at this moment, in lowland tropical rain forests, sharing for a time the habitat of jaguars and tree sloths. Oh, the tales they could tell us of exotic places: rain forest trees twelve stories tall, with huge buttressed trunks; luscious palm fruits hanging like giant grape clusters at the base of twenty-foot fronds; ancient Mayan temples and plazas, long since swallowed by the jungle.

We tend to think of these migrants as our birds, returning to us to nest each spring. But the Latin American perspective is different.

After all, many of these so-called "North American" birds spend more than half of their lives in the tropics. Perhaps they are more aptly called tropical birds who only come to visit us. In fact, the

Spanish name for the summer tanager is the same: "tangara veran-era." The pleasantly cooler and drier season between December and March, they call summer, "verano," so that this bird appears in time for their "summer" as well, though it is not necessarily the nesting season.

The life of a migrant bird is difficult, fraught with the perils of long distance travel. But it is at the destinations on either end that these species now face their greatest threat. During the last three centuries, with the nearly total destruction of the great Eastern deciduous forest of our country, species like the summer tanager have been greatly reduced in numbers. Yet sufficient numbers managed to survive in our scattered woodlots and second-growth forests. In recent decades, many mountain forest tracts have been allowed to regrow. But now, with the rapid acceleration of development in Latin America, tropical rain forests and other wintering ground habitats are disappearing at an alarming rate. These unfortunate migrants have been hit hard at both ends. Like conservation of our own forests here in the Southeast, rain forest preservation can no longer be considered somebody else's problem. Not to mention what effects rampant clear-cutting may be having on our global climate, tropical deforestation endangers the very existence of the birds that nest in our own backyards.

Fourth Week of December
Great Blue

Perhaps one of our best-known wild residents, the great blue heron embodies much that is special about living along the Southeast Coast. Its quiet, stately stance among the cordgrass is an integral part of the salt marsh mystique that wraps around our sea shore communities. Ghostlike, it haunts the dark, woody edges of marsh creeks and lagoons. Its startling call, a mix of squawk, hiss, and roar, is often heard at dusk as it leaves the waterfront to return to the communal roost tree for the night. Their rookeries have long been empty. But, despite the fact that the nesting season is far behind them, the herons' gregarious instincts still lead them, even in winter, to spend the night together in protective groupings for the sake of the safety that only numbers can provide.

Among the wading birds, the great blue is known as the patient fisherman. While its smaller cousins prance actively about scaring up killifish and mud minnows, the great blue waits majestically for larger prey to approach. Like all herons, the great blue has a noticeable kink in his spindly neck. As unwary fish swim within striking distance, the muscles that control the heron's neck movements tense up as tight as bowstrings. All of this pressure rests on this bend in the middle of the neck, where lies a "trigger bone." When the trigger is released, the sharp beak of the bird thrusts forward with lightning speed toward its mark. Usually, herons will grasp a victim in their long, pointed beaks, but occasionally great blues will actually spear larger fish. Included also in the great blue heron diet are such nonfish items as lizards, snakes, small rodents, and even hatchling alligators.

Unlike the similar-looking cranes and storks, herons and egrets (the white versions), have an almost two-dimensional body. When viewed directly from the front, they almost seem to disappear. This trait, along with their counter-shaded grayish plumage, makes the great blue difficult for fish to detect among the shadowy vegetation of the water's edge. For this reason, the great blue prefers to hunt the ecotone where water meets forest, unlike the egrets who fish the open waters, their white bodies camouflaged against the pale sky.

Although great blue herons are our tallest resident birds and have a wing span of almost six feet, they are surprisingly light. Their lanky bodies are all feathers, tendons, ligaments, and hollow bones, with proportionally little muscle mass, making flight a more feasible enterprise for such a large bird.

For short flights or when loudly threatening another heron trespassing on his fishing grounds, a great blue may be seen

flying with its neck stretched straight out, like a crane. For longer flights though, he settles into heron-cruising mode, drawing his neck into a tight loop in order to tuck his head back to his shoulders and employing slow, purposeful beats of his enormous wings. Because he has no tail with which to steer, he leaves his long legs stretched out behind him and uses his feet as a rudder. The resulting silhouette is unmistakable in the evening sky, as the winter sun sets over the tidelands of the Southeast Coast.

Conclusion
The Watery Jewel

"**A**nybody interested in a night paddle?" We were anchored on a lake miles into the wilderness. I was leading a houseboat trip through the Florida Everglades, and after a long, satisfying day of exploring the mangrove swamp by canoe, I offered the suggestion to the group as an after-dinner activity. Their response was a non-committal silence. My coleader looked at me like I was the manic naturalist—as if to say, "Can't you ever just relax?"

Still hopeful, I added: "It'll be beautiful out on the bay at night. The stars look good. Maybe we'll even see some manatees." "Yeah," I thought, "manatees, there's a crowd-pleaser. That'll grab 'em." Perhaps taking pity on me, two of the folks raised their hands somewhat uncertainly.

The three of us launched our canoe into the windless, moonless night. The surface of the water was perfectly flat and still. The night was exceedingly dark. We paddled far enough to leave the lights of the houseboats behind. It wasn't long before we noticed that the stars really were spectacular—very clear, very bright. And there were so many. "Wow." We felt that starstruck awe that residents of the hazy, green Southeast rarely experience.

The lights of the houseboats were distant now. Surrounded by the darkness, I suggested we put up our paddles and quietly drift through the silence a bit—soak up the night. As the water stilled around us, we noticed with amazement that the stars were not only above us, but below us as well, perfectly reflected on the water's smooth, dark surface. It was breathtakingly beautiful.

It was also a bit disorienting. "Gosh … , which end is up?" The impression was immediate: we were aboard a needle-nosed starship drifting through deep space. From every direction, above and below, the distant suns of heaven cast their clear pinpoints of light. There were no mangroves, no islands, no tree line, no horizon, just a universe full of stars.

I decided to forgo the usual plan of shining for eyes, listening for toadfish, and calling for screech owls. Seize the moment. I looked up toward Pegasus. The Andromeda Galaxy was as clear as I'd ever seen it—a fuzzy blotch, a worn spot on the hem of Andromeda's dark, sparkling gown. We leaned back against the thwarts and gazed upwards.

In a quiet voice I began to speak of the enormity of the universe. "All the stars we can see tonight are distant suns within our own immense spiral galaxy of slowly whirling stars. Astronomers estimate the number of stars in our galaxy to be well over one hundred billion. To put that number into perspective, you could say that there are more stars in our galaxy than the number of seconds that have passed since the birth of Christ."

"And they say our galaxy, the Milky Way, is an average size as galaxies go. Our galaxy is just one of many, many galaxies in the universe." I pointed out the Andromeda Galaxy. "Right there is a galaxy similar in size and shape to our own. It is one of the closest galaxies to the Milky Way. That fuzzy spot is the distant light from a cluster of over a hundred billion stars. From other galaxies such as that one, our galaxy must look very similar. Astronomers estimate that 'at least one hundred billion' is also the approximate number of galaxies in the universe—a universe of over a hundred billion galaxies, each with over a hundred billion stars."

With billions of light-years of lifeless space in every direction, our minds floated freely through the cosmos. We contemplated the vastness of space: infinite distances of interstellar emptiness punctuated at rare intervals by the cold surfaces of inorganic matter, pitted asteroids, luminous moons of dead rock, the white-hot atomic furnaces of suns, radioactive quasars and gaseous nebula, and then the immense galaxies and the immeasurable intergalactic void that separates them. "God … , it's all so vast ." And then those inevitable questions began to arise in our tiny souls. "Where does it end?" "Where does it begin?" "When did it all begin?" "Why did it all begin?" "What does it all mean?"

As we lost ourselves in the far reaches of a stark, inanimate universe, suddenly there was a sound in the dark water, mere feet from our recumbent heads—a sound, rich and fluid and organic, full of life, the very force of life—the deep exhalation of a very large earth creature, the breath of a manatee.

"What was that?" In that instant, in one brief nanosecond, the focus of our minds leapt, as if through hyperspace, from the outer limits of lifeless space to the rich, wet, organic island that is our home planet. Although we could not see the manatee in the dark, the thrill of being so close to such a rare and cherished gentle giant was enhanced by a sudden, deep insight into the extraordinary specialness of our world: the unique dwelling place of a thriving diversity of life forms, the wet, green planet—a watery jewel set in the black fabric of space.

Given apparently infinite time in a universe of such immense proportions, surely somewhere, somewhere amidst the stars, the miraculous has happened. Against all odds, life has begun. Somewhere in the universe are sentient folks looking up at the starry night and wondering "Why?" They are wondering "How?" They are struck with awe by the enormity of it all. They are feeling a little lonely. They are feeling small. For all they know, they alone are alive. Yet they are alive. And they are us.

About the Author

 BRUCE LOMBARDO has degrees in biology and education from the University of Cincinnati and has served as a ranger and naturalist at several state and national parks across the country, including Assateague Island and the Everglades. He also served as program director for Wilderness Southeast, Inc., in Savannah, Georgia, for six years, leading natural history trips to wild places throughout the Southeast and Latin America. As a writer for the *Georgia Guardian*, he wrote "The Wild Side," a weekly nature column about the wildlife of the Southeast.

Lombardo is especially fond of wet and woody places, and his two favorite spots on earth are the Okefenokee Swamp and the várzea of the Amazon Basin, where he loves to sit neck-deep in the flooded rain forest and watch the snakes swim by. He and his wife, Miriam Litchfield, also an environmental educator, have just completed three years of teaching biology and science in Bogotá, Colombia, and are now teaching at the Harare International School in Zimbabwe.

About the Illustrator

CAROL JOHNSON-UNSER started drawing sea gulls and other creatures of nature as a child growing up on the beaches of Long Island's south shore. After a liberal arts education at Randolph-Macon Woman's College in Virginia, she studied commercial art in New York. She was art coordinator of the University of Georgia's Marine Science Center, where she was also extensively involved in the archaeology/paleontology education programs. As an accomplished artist working in most media, Ms. Johnson-Unser has had her work exhibited through the country, and has provided illustrations for a variety of magazines, science journals, and books, including *A Field Guide to Jekyll Island, A Guide to the Georgia Coast,* and *A Journey of Hope.* She now lives with her husband on the Oregon coast, where she currently teaches nature study courses at Lane Community College in Florence.

Index